WHOLE GRAINS AROUND THE WORLD

An Oldways 4-Week Menu Plan

Acknowledgments

Thank You

We want to thank the members of the Oldways Whole Grains Council for their generous support in helping us to promote the remarkable health benefits and the delicious flavors of whole grains. We are also grateful to our scientific advisors, for keeping us up to date on the latest whole grain research, and to our culinary advisors, for sharing their creative whole grain cooking tips and tricks, and for being a constant source of culinary inspiration. A special appreciation goes to Shannon Evins and Christina Kim for helping with the nutrition analysis, and a special thanks to Petra Andersson-Pardini for her beautiful graphic design.

For information on special discounts for bulk purchases or opportunities to co-brand this book for your patients, clients, or customers, please email store@oldwayspt.org.

ISBN-13: 978-0-9858939-4-1

Every effort has been made to ensure that the information in this book is complete and accurate. However, this book is not intended as a substitute for consulting with your physician. All matters regarding your health require medical supervision. The authors will not be liable for any loss or damage allegedly arising from any information or suggestion in this book.

Table of Contents

Oldways and the Whole Grains Council

Oldways is on a mission to bring traditional foods, foodways and lifestyles—ones that are good for people and good for the planet—to people around the world. Time-honored ways of eating are dying out around the globe, as packaged foods replace the delicious dishes our ancestors passed on from generation to generation.

We founded nonprofit education organization Oldways more than 25 years ago to preserve these traditions and to show people that we can have both—good taste *and* good health when it comes to food choices. In our early days, we created the Mediterranean Diet Pyramid in partnership with the Harvard School of Public Health, and we educated health professionals, journalists, chefs, and home cooks about this delicious and nutritious cuisine. Since then, with input from nutrition scientists and expert chefs, we've created cultural food pyramids and educational resources for African Heritage diets, Asian diets, and Latin American Heritage diets, each of which these distinct cuisines is spotlighted with a chapter in this book.

Whole grains are no strangers to us at Oldways. Embracing traditional diets means embracing a diet with more whole grains. Whether it's teff and sorghum in Africa, bulgur and barley in the Mediterranean, rice and millet in Asia, or quinoa and corn in Latin America, whole grains form the backbone of cultures and cuisines all over the world. In fact, because whole grains are so central to the traditional diets that Oldways promotes, we created the Oldways Whole Grains Council in 2003, to encourage people everywhere to enjoy more whole grains.

Let the 'old ways' be your guide to good health, with this book which brings together Oldways' deep knowledge of traditional diets with the Whole Grains Council's passion for whole grains.

Introduction

Across the country, as people have begun eating more oatmeal, whole wheat toast, and brown rice, they wonder how they can go beyond the basics and explore whole grains more widely. One good place to start is by exploring the eating patterns of cultures around the world, using their heritages as a guide to good health and well-being.

Each of the four weeks in this menu plan is inspired by a different heritage diet:

Week 1: Mediterranean Diet
Scientists have studied the health benefits of the Mediterranean diet for more than half a century. Key elements of the Mediterranean diet include lots of vegetables and fruits, herbs, seafood, olive oil, beans, and whole grains. Mediterranean whole grains are often wheat-based, including bulgur, freekeh, farro, spelt, whole wheat couscous, and whole wheat breads and pastas. Barley and brown rice are widely eaten throughout the Mediterranean.

Week 2: African Heritage
The ancestors of African Americans brought many wonderful food traditions to parts of the Caribbean, South America, and the Southern states of the U.S. Though specific dishes vary from region to region, unifying characteristics of African Heritage Diets include lots of vegetables (especially leafy greens), fresh fruits, roots and tubers (such as sweet potatoes), nuts and peanuts, beans of all kinds, and staple grain foods. Ancient grains like teff, millet, and sorghum have a rich culinary history across the African diaspora, used in flatbreads, porridges, and other mixed dishes, while brown rice is also common.

Week 3: Latin American Heritage
Variations of this diet have traditionally existed in the parts of Latin America where maize (corn), potatoes, peanuts, and beans are grown. Fresh fruits and vegetables are heavily featured, as are peppers, squash, seafood, rice, and beans. Meat is traditionally used as a garnish, while plant foods make up the bulk of the meal. Latin American whole grains include brown rice and corn (especially in tortillas), as well as ancient grains like quinoa and amaranth.

Week 4: Asian Heritage
Although each Asian country has a distinct cooking style, there are many similar elements, including vegetables, fruits, strong spices, soy, rice, noodles, and seafood. This vegetable-centric diet is linked with numerous health benefits. Though white rice is common today, most folks in Asia were accustomed to brown rice and other whole grains until the late 1800's, when steel roller milling made it easy to rub off the grain's nutritious bran. Other whole grains in Asia include black rice and red rice, millet, soba (Japanese buckwheat noodles) and whole wheat. In Southeast Asia, many of the traditional flatbreads that you'll find today are made from atta, or whole wheat flour.

How to Use This Book

In this book, we encourage people to branch out and to try new foods and ingredients. There are a variety of skill levels represented in these recipes, so pick and choose the foods that appeal to you. There's no need to eat these specific foods, or follow these menus dish for dish. The Mediterranean week is more seafood-heavy, while the Latin American week is more bean-based, so feel free to mix up the flavors as you travel across the globe through the pages in our book.

Dinner recipes will generally serve four, while most breakfasts, lunches and snacks will serve one; we've noted the yield with each recipe. Leftovers from dinner can be enjoyed for lunch the next day. However, we've also included an additional recipe option at lunch. Some of our breakfast ideas are a bit more elaborate, so if you're rushed in the morning, we suggest that you to use our 1-2-3 plan to build your own healthy breakfast.

BREAKFAST 1-2-3 PLAN

A balanced breakfast includes (1) whole grains, (2) fruit, and (3) a protein source, such as milk, yogurt, nuts, legumes, or an egg. Use this 1-2-3 plan to customize the morning meal to your preferences. Just choose one item from each of the categories every day. For items that are especially prominent in different heritage diets, we've noted them with Af (African Heritage), As (Asian Heritage), La (Latin American Heritage), or Me (Mediterranean)

1 Whole Grains

Whole grain bagel
Whole grain cereal
Whole grain English muffin
Whole grain corn grits
Whole grain muffin
Whole grain pancake
or waffle
Whole grain pita bread (Me)
Whole grain toast (La, Me)
Whole wheat or corn
tortilla (La)
Granola
Oatmeal
Quinoa porridge (La)
Brown rice porridge (As)

2 Fruits

Apple (As, Me)
Banana (La)
Berries (Me, La, As, Af)
Cherries (As, Me)
Figs (Me)
Grapefruit (Me)
Grapes (As, La, Me)
Mango (Af, As, La)
Melon (Me)
Orange (As, Me)
Papaya (Af, As, La)
Peach (As, Me)
Pear (As, Me)
Pineapple (Af, La)
Raisins (As, Me)

3 Protein

Almonds (As, Me)
Beans (Af, As, La, Me)
Cheese (Me)
Cashews (Af, As)
Cottage Cheese
Eggs (As, La, Me)
Hummus (Af, Me)
Milk or Soymilk
Peanut butter
(or other nut butter)
Pistachios (As, Me)
Pumpkin Seeds (As, La)
Walnuts
Yogurt (As, Me)

Why Whole Grains?

Explore the numerous reasons to add more whole grains to your diet, from their fuller, nuttier taste to their wide-ranging health and environmental benefits.

Whole Grains: First Choice for Flavor

Unlike refined grains and flours, which simply disappear into the background, whole grains and whole grain flours actually have a distinct flavor, and a decadent one at that. As pastry chef Alice Medrich writes In her award-winning book, *Flavor Flours*, "I was startled at the delicate textures and aromas I found in the simplest cakes made from their flours. I never dreamed that a plain oat flour sponge cake would taste like butterscotch, or that a brown rice sponge could have such a moist and delicate butter flavor, or that buckwheat would have notes of honey and rose."

Other leading chefs and cookbook authors are joining the chorus of praise for whole grains:

"When I switched to whole grains, the greatest revelation was a world of flavor I had been stubbornly resisting for years."
– Alice Waters, *My Pantry*

"I don't eat whole grains because they are healthy, or wholesome, or to reap their nutritional benefits. To me, whole grains carry luxurious qualities: lively textures, vivid colors, and rich flavors."
– Maria Speck, *Ancient Grains for Modern Meals*

"My kids told me to throw out all other brownie recipes and only make the teff ones from now on, and they literally licked their bowls clean of the creamy tomato soup made with creamed brown rice. My husband learned that he loves freekeh in his frittatas, and that a layer cake made with whole-wheat pastry flour tastes more chocolatey than one made with all-purpose; it's become such a favorite that it's now his birthday cake."
– Ann Taylor Pittman, *Everyday Whole Grains*

"Who needs white rice when you have nutty, fragrant brown rice, sweet and earthy black rice, or Wehani red rice, with its hint of chestnuts and spice? If you want a beautifully composed plate or a gorgeous bed for a simple piece of fish or meat, nothing beats whole grains."
– Robin Asbell, *The Whole Grain Promise*

WHOLE GRAINS ARE GOOD FOR YOU

Whole grains are linked with **less inflammation** (ranking best among all 37 food groups studied) and **slower cognitive decline in aging.** Healthy diets with whole grains may also **reduce the risk of Alzheimer's disease by up to 54%.**
2016 Ozawa M et al., 2015 Morris MC et al.

Those eating the most whole grains had a **14% lower risk of stroke** than those eating the least whole grains.
2015 Fang L et al.

Greater servings of whole grains at breakfast are significantly related to **higher scores in reading comprehension and fluency, and math** in elementary students.
2015 Ptomey LT et al.

Increasing whole grain food intake by about 3 servings is linked with a **19-22% lower risk of heart disease.**
2016 Aune D et al.

Replacing 5% of daily calories from saturated fat (like butter, cream, and red meat) with whole grains is associated with a **9% lower risk of heart disease.**
2015 Li Y et al.

Fiber from whole grains is thought to be the most protective type of fiber against type 2 diabetes. For every additional 10g of total fiber or cereal fiber (the fiber in whole grains), the **risk of type 2 diabetes is 9% or 25% lower,** respectively.
2015 InterAct Consortium

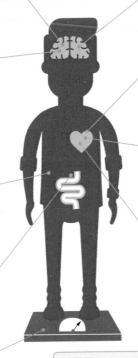

Patients on statins who also eat more than 1 serving of whole grains per day have non-HDL cholesterol (a combination of LDL and VLDL, or "bad cholesterol") levels that are **11 mg/dL lower** than those taking statins but not eating as much whole grain.
2014 Hang H et al.

Whole grains can help **improve gut bacteria.**
2016 Falony G et al., 2015 Vitaglione P et al.

Those eating the most whole grains have a **lower BMI and waist circumference,** and are less likely to be overweight or obese.
2016 Albertson AM et al.

LIVE LONGER WITH WHOLE GRAINS!

Compared to people who eat the least whole grains, people who eat the most whole grains have a 16-18% lower risk of death from all causes, 18% lower risk of death from heart disease, and 12% lower risk of death from cancer.
2016 Aune D et al., 2016 Zong G et al.

COMPARED TO ENRICHED WHEAT, WHOLE WHEAT HAS...

28% more protein	**3x** more Potassium	**3x** more Zinc	**4x** more Fiber	**6x** more Magnesium
Protein helps build and repair muscles, and is important for every cell in our body.	Potassium helps offset sodium's effect on blood pressure, and is also important for our nerves and muscles.	Zinc keeps our immune system healthy, and helps kids grow and develop.	Fiber feeds our friendly gut bacteria, and supports a healthy digestive system.	Magnesium helps normalize our blood pressure and also helps muscles relax after exercise.

87% of those who NEARLY ALWAYS CHOOSE WHOLE GRAINS FOODS HAVE INCREASED their consumption compared to 5 YEARS AGO

Although **37%** of people cited TASTE AS A BARRIER...

40% of people said TASTE was a reason they CHOOSE WHOLE GRAINS

Data from the Oldways 2015 Whole Grain Consumer Insights Survey

REFERENCES:

Albertson AM, Reicks M, Joshi N, et al. Whole grain consumption trends and associations with body weight measures in the United States: results from the cross sectional National Health and Nutrition Examination Survey 2001-2012. *Nutr J.* 2016 Jan 22;15:8.

Aune D, Keum N, Giovannucci E, et al. Whole grain consumption and risk of cardiovascular disease, cancer, and all cause and cause specific mortality: systematic review and dose-response meta-analysis of prospective studies. *BMJ.* 2016;353.

Falony G, Joossens M, Vieira-Silva S, et al. Population-level analysis of gut microbiome variation. *Science.* 2016;352(6285):560-4.

InterAct Consortium. Dietary fibre and incidence of type 2 diabetes in eight European countries: the EPIC-InterAct Study and a meta-analysis of prospective studies. *Diabetologia.* 2015;58(7):1394-408.

Li Y, Hruby A, Bernstein A, et al. Saturated Fats Compared With Unsaturated Fats and Sources of Carbohydrates in Relation to Risk of Coronary Heart Disease. *J Am Coll Cardiol.* 2015;66(14):1538-1548.

Liqun Fang, Wen Li, Wenjie Zhang, et al. Association between whole grain intake and stroke risk: evidence from a meta-analysis. *Int J Clin Exp Med.* 2015; 8(9): 16978–16983.

Morris MC, Tangney CC, Wang Y, et al. MIND diet associated with reduced incidence of Alzheimer's disease. *Alzheimers Dement.* 2015;11(9):1007-14.

Ozawa M, Shipley M, Kivimaki M, et al. Dietary pattern, inflammation and cognitive decline: The Whitehall II prospective cohort study. *Clin Nutr.* 2016;pic: S0261-5614(16)00035-2.

Ptomey LT, Steger FL, Schubert MM, et al. Breakfast Intake and Composition Is Associated with Superior Academic Achievement in Elementary Schoolchildren. *J Am Coll Nutr.* 2016;35(4):326-33.

Vitaglione P, Mennella I, Ferracane R, et al. Whole-grain wheat consumption reduces inflammation in a randomized controlled trial on overweight and obese subjects with unhealthy dietary and lifestyle behaviors: role of polyphenols bound to cereal dietary fiber. *Am J Clin Nutr.* 2015;101(2):251-61.

Wang H, Lichtenstein AH, Lamon-Fava S, et al. Association between statin use and serum cholesterol concentrations is modified by whole-grain consumption: NHANES 2003-2006. *Am J Clin Nutr.* 2014 Oct;100(4):1149-57.

Zong G, Gao A, Hu FB, et al. Whole Grain Intake and Mortality From All Causes, Cardiovascular Disease, and Cancer: A Meta-Analysis of Prospective Cohort Studies. *Circulation.* 2016;133(24):2370-80.

WHOLE GRAINS ARE ESSENTIAL TO SUSTAINABLE DIETS

Grains are the most important source of food worldwide, and are some of the least intensive foods to produce. Grains provide nearly 50% of the energy (calories) consumed by the world's population, so without them we would have no way to feed all 7.7 billion of us.

As scientists weigh the risks and benefits of different food production systems, it is easy to see why grains have been at the core of traditional diets for thousands of years. They're irreplaceable. Fruits and vegetables, while very nutritious, aren't as energy-dense as grains and are harder to grow, transport, and store for year-round enjoyment. Raising animals for meat production requires a substantial amount of land and water. Without grains, these more energy-intensive foods would put an impossible burden on our planet's precious resources.

WHOLE GRAINS PROVIDE MORE FOOD, LESS WASTE

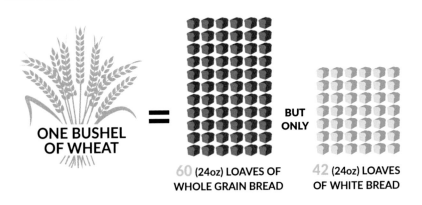

ONE BUSHEL OF WHEAT **=** 60 (24oz) LOAVES OF WHOLE GRAIN BREAD **BUT ONLY** 42 (24oz) LOAVES OF WHITE BREAD

ONE KG OF PADDY RICE **YIELDS** 750 GRAMS BROWN RICE **BUT ONLY** 650 GRAMS WHITE RICE

WATER NEEDED TO PRODUCE ONE CALORIE OF FOOD

BEEF	
FRUIT	
VEGETABLES	
GRAINS	

0   2   4   6   8   10
GALLONS

Many of the driest regions in the world depend on hardy grain crops when water is limited.

ANCIENT GRAINS ARE MORE TOLERANT OF EXTREME WEATHER. FOR EXAMPLE:

- MILLET has one of the lowest water requirements of any grain crop.
- TEFF thrives in drought and also grows well in water-logged soils.

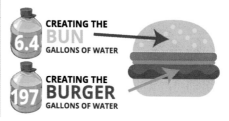

CREATING THE
6.4 BUN
GALLONS OF WATER

CREATING THE
197 BURGER
GALLONS OF WATER

WHOLE GRAINS SUPPORT BETTER LAND USE & HEALTHY SOIL

EATING MORE GRAIN-BASED MEALS **COULD FEED MORE PEOPLE WITH LESS LAND.**

75% of global agricultural land is used for animal products which only supply **17%** of our food (in calories).

OLDWAYS
WHOLE GRAINS COUNCIL

IMPROVE SOIL FERTILITY

Rotating crops with whole grains like barley, oats, rye, and triticale in the off-season can help protect against soil erosion, and also deliver nutrients back to the soil.

WHOLEGRAINSCOUNCIL.ORG

SOURCES:

60 Loaves vs 42 Loaves:
"Fast Facts," National Association of Wheat Growers, accessed December 2, 2016, http://www.wheatworld.org/wheat-info/fast-facts/.

Beef & Grain Production Water Usage:
Mesfin M. Mekonnen and Arjen Y. Hoekstra, "A global assessment of the water footprint of farm animal products," Ecosystems 15 (2012):401-415.

Millet & Teff Agricultural Requirements:
Board on Science and Technology for International Development and National Research Council, Lost Crops of Africa: Volume 1: Grains, (Washington, D.C.: National Academies Press, 1996).

75% of Land for 17% of Calories:
Mario Herrero and Philip K. Thornton, "Livestock and global change: Emerging issues for sustainable food systems," Proceedings of the National Academy of Sciences 110, no. 52 (2013): 20879, accessed December 2, 2016, doi:10.1073/pnas.1321844111

Hans Hurni, et al., "Key Implications of Land Conversions in Agriculture", Wake Up Before It Is Too Late, Trade and Development Review 2013, UNCTAD, 221, http://unctad.org/en/PublicationsLibrary/ditcted2012d3_en.pdf

Improves Soil Fertility:
Sarah Carlson and Amber Anderson, "Cover crops do double duty: cover and grain," Practical Farmers of Iowa, Research Report, March 3, 2012.

A grain is considered a whole grain as long as all three original, edible parts—the bran, the germ, and the endosperm—are still present in the same proportions as when the grain was growing in the field.

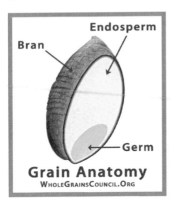

Grain Anatomy
WHOLEGRAINSCOUNCIL.ORG

THE BRAN
The bran is the multi-layered outer skin of the edible kernel. It contains important antioxidants, B vitamins, and fiber.

THE GERM
The germ is the embryo which has the potential to sprout into a new plant. It contains many B vitamins, some protein, minerals, and healthy fats.

THE ENDOSPERM
The endosperm is the germ's food supply, which provides essential energy to the young plant so it can send roots down for water and nutrients, and send sprouts up for sunlight's photosynthesizing power. The endosperm is by far the largest portion of the kernel. It contains starchy carbohydrates, proteins, and small amounts of vitamins and minerals.

What is a "Refined Grain?"

The term "refined grain" refers to grains that are not whole, because they are missing one or more of their three key parts (bran, germ, or endosperm). White flour and white rice are refined grains, for instance, because both have had their bran and germ removed, leaving only the endosperm. Refining a grain removes about a quarter of the protein in a grain, and half to two thirds or more of a score of nutrients, leaving the grain a mere shadow of its original self.

In the late 1800s, when new milling technology allowed the bran and germ to be easily and cheaply separated from the endosperm, most of the grains around the world began being eaten as refined grains. This quickly led to widespread nutrition problems, like the deficiency diseases pelagra and beri-beri.

Enriched Grains

In response, many governments recommended or required that refined grains be "enriched." Enrichment adds back less than a half dozen of the many missing nutrients, and does so in proportions different than they originally existed. Now that we more fully understand the huge health advantages of whole grains, we know that the optimal solution is simply to eat grains in their original, unrefined state.

The following charts compare whole wheat flour to refined wheat flour and enriched wheat flour, and brown rice to white and enriched rice. You can see the vast difference in essential nutrients.

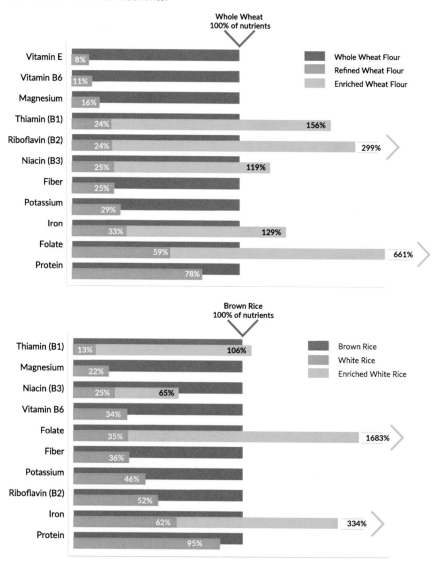

Whole Wheat
100% of nutrients

- Whole Wheat Flour
- Refined Wheat Flour
- Enriched Wheat Flour

Nutrient	Value
Vitamin E	8%
Vitamin B6	11%
Magnesium	16%
Thiamin (B1)	24% / 156%
Riboflavin (B2)	24% / 299%
Niacin (B3)	25% / 119%
Fiber	25%
Potassium	29%
Iron	33% / 129%
Folate	59% / 661%
Protein	78%

Brown Rice
100% of nutrients

- Brown Rice
- White Rice
- Enriched White Rice

Nutrient	Value
Thiamin (B1)	13% / 106%
Magnesium	22%
Niacin (B3)	25% / 65%
Vitamin B6	34%
Folate	35% / 1683%
Fiber	36%
Potassium	46%
Riboflavin (B2)	52%
Iron	62% / 334%
Protein	95%

Why Whole Grains? (continued)

Whole Wheat vs. Whole Grain

We get asked regularly, "What is the difference between whole wheat and whole grain?" Our answer is another question: "What is the difference between a carrot and a vegetable?"

Everyone knows that carrots are vegetables, but not all vegetables are carrots. It's similar with whole wheat and whole grain: Whole wheat is one kind of whole grain, so all whole wheat is whole grain, but not all whole grains are whole wheat.

IF YOU'RE READING THIS IN CANADA

Canada has a unique regulatory situation relative to whole wheat flour. Canada allows wheat flour to be called "whole wheat" even when up to 5% of the original kernel is missing. So, in Canada you'll hear two terms used:

- Whole Wheat Flour in Canada—contains at least 95% of the original kernel
- Whole Grain Whole Wheat Flour in Canada—contains 100% of the original kernel

"Whole grain whole wheat flour" would be redundant in the U.S.A. Whole wheat flour is always whole grain in the States. But not in Canada, so be aware.

GLUTEN FREE WHOLE GRAINS

First Things First: What is Gluten?

Humans have been eating gluten for eons. Gluten-forming proteins are found naturally in wheat (including ancient wheats like einkorn, farro, Kamut®, or spelt), barley, and rye. They help dough stretch and bread rise.

Whether or not you follow a gluten-free diet, you might be surprised to learn that most whole grains are naturally gluten-free:

Amaranth	Millet	Rice
Buckwheat	*Oats	Sorghum
Corn	Quinoa	Teff
		Wild Rice

*Oats are naturally gluten-free, but are often cross-contaminated with gluten during growing or processing. Check the label to be sure.

Very Few People Need a Gluten-Free or Wheat-Free Diet for Medical Reasons

Celiac disease, which affects an estimated 1–2% of the US population, is a medically diagnosable autoimmune disease that requires strict lifetime adherence to a gluten-free diet. Another 0.2–0.4% of Americans are allergic to wheat (but not barley or rye).

What About Gluten-Sensitivity?

Many people who respond well to a gluten-free diet, but don't test positive for celiac disease, are sometimes thought to have "non-celiac gluten sensitivity." But science is casting doubts on the usefulness of gluten-free diets for people like these. Recently, researchers analyzed data from 10 studies, in which 1,312 adults with "non-celiac gluten sensitivity" were tested for their reaction to gluten. In these 10 double-blind, placebo-controlled gluten challenges (in which neither the researchers nor the participants knew if they were getting a gluten-free diet or the gluten-containing control/placebo), only 16% of the patients showed gluten-specific symptoms when they ate the gluten-containing diet, and 40% of them had similar or increased symptoms when on the gluten-free control diet. In other words, gluten is probably not the culprit for what people consider gluten sensitivity: In fact, blaming gluten may keep other serious problems from being addressed.

How to Find & Store Whole Grains

THE WHOLE GRAIN STAMP: AN AID FOR BUSY SHOPPERS

Now that we've made the case for eating more whole grains, we'll help you find them in the store. Years ago, spotting whole grains was difficult, with packages covered with unverified claims. To solve that problem, the Oldways Whole Grains Council created the Whole Grain Stamp packaging symbol in 2005.

There are three different varieties of the Whole Grain Stamp: the 100% Stamp, the 50%+ Stamp, and the Basic Stamp.

- If a product bears the **100% Stamp** (left image below), then **all of its grain is whole grain.** There is a minimum requirement of 16g (16 grams)—a full serving— of whole grain per labeled serving, for products using the 100% Stamp.

- If a product bears the **50%+ Stamp** (middle image), then **at least half its grain is whole grain.** There is a minimum requirement of 8g (8 grams)—a half serving—of whole grain per labeled serving, for products using the 50%+ Stamp. This stamp was added to the Whole Grain Stamp family in January of 2017, and it began appearing on products in the summer of 2017.

- If a product bears **the Basic Stamp** (right image), it contains at least 8g (8 grams) —a half serving—of whole grain, but also contains some refined grain.

Each Stamp also shows how many grams of whole grain ingredients are in a serving of the product. While the images below show just three different examples of possible gram amounts (23g, 32g, 20g), when you look on your grocery shelves you'll see a wide range of numbers, reflecting the whole grain content of a serving of that specific product. If a product contains large amounts of whole grain (23g, 37g, 41g, etc.) but also contains extra bran, germ, or refined flour, it will use the 50%+ Stamp or the Basic Stamp (and not the 100% Stamp).

100% OF THE GRAIN IS WHOLE GRAIN **50% OR MORE OF THE GRAIN IS WHOLE GRAIN** **EAT 48g OR MORE OF WHOLE GRAIN DAILY**

From 2005 through 2016, before the introduction of the 50%+ Stamp, Basic Stamp products may have contained mostly whole grain. Until all packaging is updated, you may see some products still bearing the Basic Stamp even though more than 50% of their grain is whole grain!

As of mid-2017, more than 11,000 products are registered to use the Whole Grain Stamp. Search the database at www.wholegrainscouncil.org/products

IF YOU'RE READING THIS IN CANADA

In Canada, the 100% Stamp can only appear on products in which 100% of the ingredients are whole grain. This means that in Canada, a bag of brown rice, or a sack of whole grain flour, or a box of oatmeal can use the 100% Stamp, as long as these products have no added non-whole-grain ingredients. Similarly, in Canada, the 50%+ Stamp can only appear on products in which at least half of the product (by weight) is whole grain.

FIND WHOLE GRAINS NEAR YOU

People often email us asking, "Where can I find teff in Miami?" or "Is there a store in Des Moines that sells farro?" We can't track the options in every community, but we can help you find mail-order sources for intact, un-processed whole grains and the whole grain flours and meals milled from them.

Check out our list at www.wholegrainscouncil.org/mail

STORING WHOLE GRAINS

Food tastes best when it's fresh. Luckily, whole intact grains are built for storage, so they tend to have a longer shelf life than nearly any other unprocessed food. Still, we recommend only buying what you will reasonably be able to eat in six months or so, since whole grains contain healthy oils that can be negatively affected by heat, light, and moisture. As with all whole foods from nature, some of the nutrients in grains inevitably fade away over time.

How long your grains will stay fresh at home can depend largely on how much of their shelf-life has already been used up at the warehouse and the store, before you bring them home. This means there are no absolute freshness guarantees. In general, whole grain flours spoil more quickly than intact grains, because their protective bran layer has been broken up, allowing oxygen to reach all parts of the grain. Below you'll find some guidelines culled from a variety of experts that may help.

WHOLE GRAIN STORAGE CHART

	INTACT WHOLE GRAIN (BERRIES OR GROATS)	WHOLE GRAIN FLOUR/ MEAL
Amaranth	Pantry: 4 months Freezer: 8 months	Pantry: 2 months Freezer: 4 months
Barley	Pantry: 6 months Freezer: 1 year	Pantry: 3 months Freezer: 6 months
Brown/colored rice	Pantry: 6 months Freezer: 1 year	Pantry: 3 months Freezer: 6 months
Buckwheat	Pantry: 2 months Freezer: 4 months	Pantry: 1 month Freezer: 2 months
Corn/Popcorn	Pantry: 6 months Freezer: 1 year	Pantry: 3 months Freezer: 6 months
Farro	Pantry: 6 months Freezer: 1 year	Pantry: 3 months Freezer: 6 months
Millet	Pantry: 2 months Freezer: 4 months	Pantry: 1 month Freezer: 2 months
Oats	Pantry: 4 months Freezer: 8 months	Pantry: 2 months Freezer: 4 months
Quinoa	Pantry: 4 months Freezer: 8 months	Pantry: 2 months Freezer: 4 months
Rye	Pantry: 6 months Freezer: 1 year	Pantry: 3 months Freezer: 6 months
Sorghum	Pantry: 4 months Freezer: 8 months	Pantry: 2 months Freezer: 4 months
Spelt	Pantry: 6 months Freezer: 1 year	Pantry: 3 months Freezer: 6 months
Teff	Pantry: 4 months Freezer: 8 months	Pantry: 2 months Freezer: 4 months
Wheat, including Bulgur, Freekah	Pantry: 6 months Freezer: 1 year	Pantry: 3 months Freezer: 6 months
Wild Rice	Pantry: 4 months Freezer: 8 months	Pantry: 2 months Freezer: 4 months

Cooking Whole Grains, A to Z

THE A-Z GUIDE TO COOKING WITH WHOLE GRAINS

AMARANTH

Cook 1 cup dry grain with: 2 cups liquid (expands to 2½ cups cooked grain)

Cook Time: Bring to boil, then simmer 15–20 minutes

Best Uses: Porridge or polenta-style recipes. Great thickener for stews. Can also be popped like popcorn. Tiny sized grains almost burst between your teeth. Not well suited for grain salads or pilafs.

Flavor Profile: Peppery taste, with a pleasantly sweet, grassy aroma. Pairs well with squash, corn, sesame, cinnamon, vanilla, and chocolate.

Gluten-free? Yes

History: Technically a pseudo-grain, amaranth is a staple of the Aztecs, with a long history in Mexican and Peruvian cuisines (later becoming popular in Nepal, India, and other countries). It's typically enjoyed as breakfast porridge throughout Latin America and Southeast Asia, but in Mexico, it's also served popped with honey, as a sweet snack called allegria.

Nutrition in 1 serving (¼ cup uncooked): 180 calories, 3g fiber, 7g protein. Excellent source of magnesium, manganese and phosphorus. Good source of iron, copper, selenium, and Vitamin B6.

Recipe Ideas:

» Amaranth with Peppers and Cabbage (page 72)

» Banana Amaranth Porridge (page 78)

BARLEY (LOOK FOR "WHOLE GRAIN," "HULLED," OR "DEHULLED")

Cook 1 cup dry grain with: 3 cups liquid (expands to 3½ cups cooked grain)

Cook Time: Bring to boil, then simmer 45–60 minutes (some brands recommend an overnight soak)

Best Uses: Pleasantly firm chew makes it ideal for grain salads and pilafs. Great substitute for rice, especially in curries, stir fries, and risottos. (Note that pearled barley is not whole grain.)

Flavor Profile: Rich flavor with a mild sweetness. Pairs well with mushrooms, root vegetables, warm spices, and fall flavors (like apple).

Gluten-free? No

History: One of the oldest grains cultivated in the Fertile Crescent, barley (often cooked as a porridge or baked into a crude bread) was also one of the first grains eaten in the ancient cuisines of China and Egypt, and it was an important source of nutrion during Greek and Roman times.

Nutrition in 1 serving (¼ cup uncooked): 160 calories, 8g fiber (more than any other whole grain), 6g protein. Excellent source of manganese, selenium, and thiamin. Good source of magnesium, phosphorus, copper, and niacin.

Recipe Ideas:
- » Mediterranean Eggplant and Barley Salad (page 39)
- » Barley, Pineapple, and Jicama Salad with Avocado (page 73)

BUCKWHEAT

Cook 1 cup dry grain with: 2 cups liquid (expands to 4 cups cooked grain)

Cook Time: Bring to boil, then simmer 20 minutes

Best Uses: To keep the grains from becoming too creamy, buckwheat is often coated with an egg (or other fat) before cooking. These pyramidal shaped grains work well in casseroles, and breakfast porridges. Buckwheat flour is quite versatile, adding richness to soba noodles, pancakes, and pastries.

Flavor Profile: Robust and earthy. Pairs well with dried fruit, dark spices, beets, walnuts, and hazelnuts. Untoasted (raw) buckwheat groats have a much milder flavor than toasted buckwheat (kasha).

Gluten-free? Yes

History: Technically a pseudo-grain (it is not even related to wheat), buckwheat has a strong history in Asian and Eastern European cuisine because it can grow in cold climates. It is the grain of choice for traditonal dishes around the globe, including French crepes, Russian blini, Japanese soba noodles, and Jewish kasha. Buckwheat is also a popular cover crop, restoring the soil between seasons of farming.

Nutrition in 1 serving (¼ cup uncooked): 140 calories, 4g fiber, 5g protein. Excellent source of magnesium, copper, and manganese. Good source of phosphorus, riboflavin, and niacin.

Recipe Ideas:
- » *Buckwheat soba noodles:* Kimchi Soba Noodle Bowl (page 84)
- » *Substitute for brown rice or quinoa in the Asian Breakfast Bowl (page 90)*

BULGUR WHEAT

Cook 1 cup dry grain with: 2 cups liquid (expands to 3 cups cooked grain)

Cook Time: Bring to boil, then simmer 10–12 minutes (fine bulgur reconstitutes just by soaking)

Best Uses: The fluffy, chewy texture makes it ideal for grain salads, sides, and pilafs. Great for adding substance to light dishes. It is also delicious served warm as a creamy breakfast porridge.

Flavor Profile: Nutty, wheat flavor. Pairs well with parsley, tomatoes, cinnamon, and most fresh produce.

Gluten-free? No

History: Bulgur is wheat that's been pre-cooked then cracked into smaller pieces (hence the quick cooking time). In fact, some call it "ancient fast food." Bulgur wheat has a rich history in Eastern Mediterranean cuisine, dating back to Egypt and the Roman Empire.

Nutrition in 1 serving (¼ cup uncooked): 120 calories, 4g fiber, 4g protein. Excellent source of manganese. Good source of magnesium, phosphorus, and niacin.

Recipe Ideas:
» Tabbouleh (page 33)
» Bulgur Salad (Lunch, page 30)

CORN

Cook 1 cup dry whole grain cornmeal with: 4 cups liquid (expands to 2½ cups cooked grain)

Cook Time: Bring to boil, then simmer 25–35 minutes

Best Uses: Whole grain cornmeal is best suited for porridge or polenta-style recipes. (Note: If it says degerminated, it's not whole grain.) Great thickener for stews. Not well-suited for grain salads or pilafs. Popcorn is also considered a whole grain (although fresh corn, such as corn on the cob, is not).

Flavor Profile: Sweet taste. Pairs well with chiles, berries, stone fruit, aromatic spices, tomatoes, cumin, peppers, and beans.

Gluten-free? Yes

History: Corn is native to the Americas, and it has a rich history in Aztec, Mayan, and Native American diets.

Nutrition in 1 serving (¼ cup uncooked): 110 calories, 2g fiber, 2g protein. Good source of phosphorus, magnesium, manganese, selenium, and thiamin.

Recipe Ideas:
» *Whole grain corn tortillas:* Fish Tacos with Mango Salad (page 69)
» *Whole grain corn tostadas:* Oldways Wild Veggie Tostadas (page 67)

FREEKEH GREEN WHEAT

Cook 1 cup dry grain with: 2½ cups liquid (expands to about 2½ to 3 cups cooked grain)

Cook Time: Bring to boil, then simmer 20–25 minutes (longer if not using cracked freekeh)

Best Uses: The fluffy, chewy texture makes it ideal for grain salads, sides, and pilafs. Great for adding substance to light dishes. Flavorful grain base for meat dishes and other entrees.

Flavor Profile: Signature smoky flavor. Pairs well with Middle Eastern flavors, especially cinnamon, tomatoes, lemon, and pine nuts.

Gluten-free? No

History: Found mostly in Middle Eastern and North African cuisine, freekeh wheat traces its roots back several thousand years to ancient Egypt and surrounding areas. Legend has it that freekeh was discovered when ancient villagers in the Eastern Mediterranean hurriedly picked young wheat before an attack on their city. Attackers' fires burned the young wheat, but the result was quite delicious.

Nutrition in 1 serving (¼ cup uncooked): 160 calories, 6g fiber, 7g protein. Good source of iron.

Recipe Ideas:
- » Freekeh Pilaf (page 31)
- » Substitute for farro in the Veggie Omelet with Farro (page 34—cooking times may vary)

MILLET

Cook 1 cup dry grain with: 2½ cups liquid (expands to 4 cups fully, cooked grain)

Cook Time: Bring to boil, then simmer 25–35 minutes

Best Uses: Depending on how much liquid you use, millet can be prepared fluffy (for pilafs and grain salads), or sticky (for croquettes and patties), or creamy (for warm porridge). Millet is also a delighful base for curries, stir fries, and pilafs. Best served warm.

Flavor Profile: Buttery. Pairs well with mushrooms, herbs, warm spices, scallions, and squash.

Gluten-free? Yes

History: Millet is one of the leading staple grains of India, and it was also used in ancient Chinese noodles before wheat was domesticated. Although common in birdseed in the US, nutritous millet is also important to the cuisines of South America, Russia, the Himalayas, and Africa.

Nutrition in 1 serving (¼ cup uncooked): 190 calories, 4g fiber, 6g protein. Excellent source of manganese. Good source of magnesium, phosphorus, copper, thiamin, and niacin.

Recipe Ideas:
- » Millet with Zucchini and Chickpeas (page 48)
- » Orange Cardamom Millet Porridge (page 96)

OATS

Cook 1 cup dry steel cut oats with: 4 cups liquid (expands to 3 cups cooked grain)

Cook Time: Bring to boil, then simmer 30 minutes

Best Uses: Porridge or polenta-style recipes. Steel cut oats can also be substituted for rice in risotto style recipes. Not well suited for grain salads or pilafs.

Flavor Profile: Sweet toasty aroma with hints of butterscotch. Pairs well with cinnamon, dried and fresh fruit, thyme, mushrooms, walnuts, coffee, and coconut.

Gluten-free? Yes. (Check for certifed gluten-free oats, as oats are frequently cross contaminated with gluten during growing and processing.)

History: Oats are the porridge of choice in Scotland, Ireland, and other Northern European nations, as they grow best in cool, rainy climates. Today, most oats are steamed and flattened to produced rolled oats, quick oats, or instant oats—but all are whole grain, as the bran and germ are virtually always left intact. Oats have also been used in medicinal-type cosmetics for their anti-itching properties.

Nutrition in 1 serving (¼ cup uncooked): 150 calories, 4g fiber, 7g protein. Excellent source of phosphorous, manganese, and thiamin. Good source of iron, magnesium, zinc, and copper.

Recipe Ideas:
  » Steel Cut Oat Risotto with Mushrooms (page 41)
  » "Mosh" Guatemalan Oatmeal (page 70)

QUINOA

Cook 1 cup dry grain with: 2 cups liquid (expands to 3 cups cooked grain)

Cook Time: Bring to boil, then simmer 12–15 minutes

Best Uses: Pleasantly firm chew even when served chilled, making it ideal for both warm and cold grain salads. Popular in sides and pilafs.

Flavor Profile: Hints of grassiness. Pairs well with nearly anything, especially Latin American ingredients (corn, black beans, avocado, citrus, cilantro, peppers, and tomatoes). Be sure to rinse well before cooking, as quinoa has a bitter outer coating (saponin) that needs to be washed off.

Gluten-free? Yes

History: Technically a pseudo-grain (related to chard), quinoa was sacred to the Incas, and it has been central to Bolivian and Peruvian diets for centuries. It's primarily grown high in the Andes mountains, but some US producers are also starting to grow their own. Quinoa is one of the few plant foods that serves up a complete protein, offering all essential amino acids in a healthy balance.

Nutrition in 1 serving (¼ cup uncooked): 160 calories, 3g fiber, 6g protein. Excellent source of magnesium, phosphorus, and manganese. Good source of iron, copper, thiamin, and Vitamin B6.

Recipe Ideas:
- » Quinoa Porridge with Figs and Honey (page 54)
- » Fiesta Quinoa Salad (page 66)

RICE (BROWN RICE, BLACK RICE, RED RICE, ETC.)

Cook 1 cup dry brown rice with: 2½ cups liquid (expands to 3 cups cooked grain)

Cook Time: Bring to boil, then simmer 25–45 minutes (varies)

Best Uses: Great as a base in curries, stir fries, risottos, and rice pudding. In fried rice, brown rice needs less oil. Shorter-grain rices are stickier, making them best suited for sushi and risotto, while longer-grain rices are great for pilafs. Can also be cooked in stock until soft and starchy, then blended and substituted for heavy cream. In gluten-free baking, the bran and germ in brown-rice flour helps to make it less gummy.

Flavor Profile: Neutral, toasty flavor with hints of caramel. Accentuates other flavors, and it pairs well with nearly anything, especially eggs, milk, and chocolate.

Gluten-free? Yes

History: Rice is grown on every continent except Antarctica, and it has been a staple of cultures and cuisines for millennia. Rice provides 19% of the calories available worldwide, with an especially strong history in Asian cuisine. Whole grain rice is not just brown; it can also be red, black, or other colors.

Nutrition in 1 serving (¼ cup uncooked): 110 calories, 2g fiber, 2g protein. Good source of phosphorus, magnesium, manganese, selenium, and thiamin.

Recipe Ideas:
- » "Arroz con Pollo"—Rice with Chicken (page 77)
- » Black Rice Chicken Congee (page 87)

RYE & TRITICALE (A WHEAT-RYE HYBRID)

Cook 1 cup dry grain with: 4 cups liquid (expands to 3 cups cooked grain)

Cook Time: After soaking overnight, bring to boil, then simmer 45–60 minutes

Best Uses: Rye berries and triticale berries can be used interchangeably with wheat berries in most recipes, and they work especially well in pilafs, casseroles, and grain salads. Rye flour adds a distinct, rich flavor to baked goods, especially in yeast breasts. Rye flakes and rye grits work well in breakfast porridge or polenta-style recipes.

Flavor Profile: Rich and slightly tangy. Works well in Eastern European recipes,

especially with cabbage, beets, mustard, raisins, and sweet and sour flavors.

Gluten-free? No

History: Because rye can grow in colder climates where many other grains can't survive, it has a long tradition in the cuisines of Russia, Poland, Scandinavia, Argentina, Turkey, China, and Canada. Rye and wheat have long cross-bred in nature, but it wasn't until 1937 that the mash-up called triticale became a fertile crop. Triticale grows easily without commercial fertilizers and pesticides.

Nutrition in 1 serving (¼ cup uncooked): 140 calories, 6g fiber, 4g protein. Excellent source of manganese. Good source of magnesium, phosphorus, copper, selenium, and niacin

Recipe Ideas:

» *Substitute cooked rye or triticale for the cooked barley in the Mediterranean Eggplant and Barley Salad (page 39—cooking times may vary)*

» *Substitute for the freekeh in the Freekeh Pilaf (page 31—cooking times may vary)*

SORGHUM

Cook 1 cup dry grain with: 4 cups liquid (expands to 3 cups cooked grain)

Cook Time: Bring to boil, then simmer 25–40 minutes

Best Uses: Pleasantly firm chew makes it ideal for grain salads and pilafs. Its pearly shape makes it a great substitute for couscous. Can also be popped, like popcorn. Sorghum flour performs beautifully in pancakes, waffles, crepes, and cookies.

Flavor Profile: Sweet taste, with hints of corn or wheat flavor. Pairs especially well with Southern ingredients, like ham, bourbon, pecans, peanuts, berries, dates, figs, banana, and warm spices.

Gluten-free? Yes

History: Sorghum (also called milo) is believed to have originated in Africa, where it remains an important cereal grain, even today. It is naturally drought tolerant, making it a smart choice for diners eating with their environmental footprint in mind. Traditonally, sorghum is used in porridges, flatbreads, and even beverages.

Nutrition in 1 serving (¼ cup uncooked): 160 calories, 3g fiber, 5g protein. Excellent source of manganese. Good source of magnesium, phosphorus, selenium, and vitamin B6.

Recipe Ideas:

» Stir-Fried Thai Sorghum Bowl (page 97)

» Chilled Sorghum Salad (Lunch, page 54)

TEFF

Cook 1 cup dry grain with: 3 cups liquid (expands to 2½ cups cooked grain)

Cook Time: Bring to boil, then simmer 20 minutes

Best Uses: Porridge or polenta style recipes. Great thickener for stews. Not well suited for grain salads or pilafs. Teff flour adds a rich, cocoa flavor to baked goods.

Flavor Profile: Slightly sweet taste with undertones of cocoa and hazelnut. Pairs well with nuts, chocolate, seeds, pumpkin, and dark fruit.

Gluten-free? Yes

History: Teff is a tiny (less than 1mm) grain native to the Horn of Africa, where nomads could carry enough teff seed in their pocket to sow an entire field. In fact, its name may come from the Amharic word for "lost" because the seed is so tiny. Teff is most well known as the main ingredient in injera, the spongy flatbread that Ethiopians use in place of utensils.

Nutrition in 1 serving (¼ cup uncooked): 180 calories, 4g fiber, 6g protein. Excellent source of magnesium, copper, and manganese. Good source of iron, phosphorus, zinc, thiamin, and vitamin B6.

Recipe Ideas:
  » Maple Walnut Teff Porridge (page 60)
  » *Substitute for quinoa in Stuffed Poblanos* (page 71)

WHOLE WHEAT FLOUR (INCLUDING KAMUT®, SPELT & EINKORN FLOURS)

Best Uses: Whole wheat flour can be substituted for up to 50% of the all-purpose flour in a recipe without making adjustments. To convert a recipe to 100% whole wheat, add an extra 2 teaspoons of liquid per cup of flour, then let the dough rest for 20 minutes after mixing. White whole wheat flour has a milder flavor and lighter color. Whole wheat pastry flour and sprouted whole wheat flour are also good options for baking, while whole grain spelt flour is well suited for pasta and pastries.

Flavor Profile: Hearty and slightly nutty. Pairs well with nearly everything, especially honey, chicken, squash, mushrooms, cheese, and warm spices.

Gluten-free? No

History: Wheat is one of the earliest domesticated grains, and even today provides 19% of available calories. Breads (nearly always made from wheat) have been a mealtime staple for centuries, and whole wheat breads in particular were especially common before the advent of roller milling in the late 1800's. Wheat was to the Mediterranean what rice was to Asia and corn was to Latin America.

Nutriton in 1 serving (¼ cup flour): 100 calories, 3gfiber, 4g protein. Good source of magnesium, phosphorus, and thiamin.

Recipe Ideas:

» Egg and Veggie Paratha (page 94)

» *Whole wheat pita bread:* Mediterranean Pita Pizza (page 35)

WHEAT BERRIES & ANCIENT WHEATS: EINKORN, EMMER/FARRO, KAMUT®, & SPELT

Cook 1 cup dry grain with: 2½–4 cups liquid (expands to 3 cups cooked grain)

Cook Time: Bring to boil, then simmer 25–40 minutes (some sources recommend soaking overnight)

Best Uses: Pleasant chew even when chilled, making it ideal for both warm and cold grain salads. Popular in sides and pilafs. Farro (also called emmer) is becoming popular in risotto ("farrotto").

Flavor Profile: Nutty and slightly sweet. Pairs well with nearly anything.

Gluten-free? No

History: These ancient strains of wheat were first domesticated along the Fertile Crescent, but were largely ignored after modern dwarf wheat became popular in the mid 20th century (with the advent of the Green Revolution). Einkorn is thought to be the most ancient of wheat varieties available today, with just two sets of chromosomes (instead of six, like modern wheat).

Nutrition in 1 serving (¼ cup uncooked): 160 calories, 5g fiber, 7g protein. Excellent source of manganese, selenium, and thiamin. Good source of magnesium, phosphorus, zinc, and copper.

Recipe Ideas:

» Veggie Omelet with Farro (page 34)

» Arugula Salad with Farro and Dates (Lunch, page 42)

WILD RICE

Cook 1 cup dry grain with: 3 cups liquid (expands to 3½ cups cooked grain)

Cook Time: Bring to boil, then simmer 45–55 minutes

Best Uses: Chewy texture makes it great in grain salads and pilafs, or for adding heartiness to green salads and light dishes. You can even pop wild rice, like popcorn. Just heat it in a little oil and shake until it pops.

Flavor Profile: Aromatic, nutty flavor. Pairs well with brown rice, caramelized onions, squash, root vegetables, and mushrooms.

Gluten-free? Yes

History: Wild rice is one of the few whole grains native to North America; it originated in the area of the upper Great Lakes (in what is now both the U.S. and Canada). It is not actually related to rice, but is, instead, a wild grass. Traditionally, wild rice was harvested in canoes powered only by long poles, using beater sticks to knock the ripe seeds into the bottom of the canoes.

Nutrition in 1 serving (¼ cup uncooked): 140 calories, 3g fiber, 6g protein. Excellent source of magnesium and manganese. Good source of phosphorus, zinc, copper, niacin, and folate.

Recipe Ideas:
>> Southern-Style Chicken and Wild Rice Pilaf (page 59)
>> Oldways Wild Veggie Tostadas (page 67)

GENERAL WHOLE GRAIN COOKING TIPS

Plain Grains, General Directions

Cooking most grains is very similar to cooking rice: Place the dry grain in a pan with water or broth, bring it to a boil, then simmer until the liquid is absorbed. Pasta is generally cooked in larger amounts of water; the excess is drained after cooking.

Pasta Method

Some grains, like brown rice, farro, and wheat berries, can be cooked using the "pasta method," in which uncooked whole grains are placed in a large pot of boiling water, boiled until tender, then drained of their excess liquid. America's Test Kitchen found that this process significantly speeds up cooking (taking brown rice from 60 minutes to 35).

Shortcuts

- **Soaking:** If you want to cook grains more quickly, let them sit in the allotted amount of water for a few hours before cooking. Just before dinner, add extra water if necessary, then cook. You'll find that cooking time is shortened by pre-soaking.

- **Pre-cooking:** For steel-cut oats, try this shortcut: Bring water and oats to a boil, then turn off the heat, allow to cool, and let the oats soak overnight in the fridge. In the morning, return the oats to a boil, and they'll soften more quickly. (This approach is similar to the "two-step" cooking method popularized in Maria Speck's cookbook, *Simply Ancient Grains*.)

- **Batch cooking:** Another shortcut is to cook whole grains in big batches. Grains keep 3-4 days in the fridge and take just minutes to warm up with a little added water or broth. You can also use the leftovers for cold salads (just toss with chopped veggies, dressing, and anything else that suits your fancy), or toss a few handfuls in some canned soup. Cook once, then take it easy.

- **Quick cooking:** There are also many quick-cooking grains on the market, both in the freezer aisle and the grain aisle. These grains have been pre-cooked so some are ready in as little as 90 seconds in the microwave.

Sticky Bottoms

If whole grains are sticking to the bottom of the pan, turn off the heat, add a very small amount of liquid, put a lid on the pan, and let it sit for a few minutes. The grain will loosen, easing serving and cleanup.

Important: Time Varies

Grains can vary in cooking time depending on the age of the grain, the variety, and the pans you're using to cook. When you decide they're tender and tasty, they're done. If the grain is not as tender as you like when the recipe had indicated " time is up," simply add more water and continue cooking. Or, if everything seems fine before the liquid is all absorbed, simply drain the excess.

Mediterranean Diet Pyramid

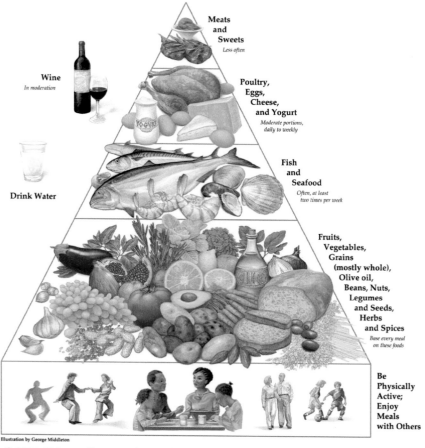

Meats and Sweets
Less often

Wine
In moderation

Poultry, Eggs, Cheese, and Yogurt
Moderate portions,
daily to weekly

Drink Water

Fish and Seafood
Often, at least
two times per week

Fruits, Vegetables, Grains (mostly whole), Olive oil, Beans, Nuts, Legumes and Seeds, Herbs and Spices
Base every meal
on these foods

Be Physically Active; Enjoy Meals with Others

Illustration by George Middleton

Day 1

Breakfast: (Serves 1) ½ cup plain Greek yogurt topped with 4 chopped figs (fresh or dried) and ¼ cup granola, or 1-2-3 Breakfast of your choice (see page 4)

Lunch: (Serves 1) ½ cup cooked bulgur tossed with ½ cup cooked (or canned) chickpeas, ½ cup chopped fresh spinach, ½ cup cubed watermelon (or fresh berries), 2 tablespoons crumbled feta, and ½ tablespoon extra-virgin olive oil. Season with salt and pepper to taste.

Dinner: Shish Kebabs over Freekeh Pilaf (recipes follow) served with ½ cup cucumber slices per person, and Dill Yogurt Sauce for dipping (page 101)

Snack: (Serves 1) ½ cup whole grain crackers with ¼ cup hummus

SHISH KEBABS (SERVES 4)

If you're cooking for one or two, repurpose the leftover chicken and veggies in a whole wheat pita with hummus for lunch the next day. Or, if you're cooking for four, just double the recipe for leftovers.

For the Marinade

- 3 tablespoons olive oil
- 1 tablespoon low-sodium soy sauce
- 1 tablespoon balsamic vinegar
- 1 tablespoon honey
- 1 clove garlic, minced

For the Kebabs

- 1 pound boneless, skinless chicken breast, cut into 1-inch cubes
- 1 8-ounce package mushrooms
- 1 orange or red bell pepper, cut into 1-inch pieces
- 1 red onion, cut into 1-inch pieces
- 1 medium zucchini, cut into 1-inch pieces

Week One: Mediterranean Diet

Mix the olive oil, soy sauce, vinegar, honey, and garlic in a medium bowl, then transfer half to a ziptop bag. Add the chicken to the bag of marinade and toss to combine, reserving the other half of the marinade in the fridge in a covered container. Allow to marinate in the refrigerator for at least 4 hours, or overnight. Soak bamboo skewers in water for 30 minutes. Pre-heat the grill on medium-high heat. Thread the meat and veggies onto skewers, leaving a bit of space between each item. Brush the remaining, unused marinade over the skewered meat and vegetables. Add the skewers to the grill and cook, turning 2 or 3 times, until the chicken is cooked, about 10–15 minutes. Serve on a bed of freekeh pilaf (recipe follows).

FREEKEH PILAF (SERVES 4)

Because freekeh is green wheat that has been roasted, it offers a signature smoky flavor unmatched by other grains. Makes enough to serve with dinner the following night, as well.

- 1 tablespoon olive oil
- ½ small onion, finely chopped
- 1 large carrot, shredded
- 1 cup cracked freekeh
- 2½ cups low-sodium vegetable broth
- ½ cup coarsely chopped walnuts, toasted

Heat the oil in a medium saucepan over medium-high heat. Add the onion and carrot and cook, stirring frequently, until the vegetables are softened, about 6 minutes. Stir in the freekeh, then add the broth and bring to a boil. Reduce the heat and simmer, covered, stirring frequently, until the liquid is absorbed, about 25 minutes (longer if not using cracked freekeh). Stir in the walnuts.

Day 2

Breakfast: (Serves 1) 1 cup cooked oatmeal topped with 4 chopped dried apricots, 1 tablespoon tahini, and 1 teaspoon honey, served with 6 ounces plain Greek yogurt, or 1-2-3 Breakfast of your choice (see page 4)

Lunch: (Serves 1) 1 small whole wheat pita, stuffed with 2 tablespoons hummus, ¼ cup chopped grilled chicken (leftover from shish kebab dinner on Day 1), and ⅓ cup grilled vegetables (leftover from shish kebab dinner on Day 1), served with 1 pear.

Dinner: Herb Baked Fish (recipe follows) served with Freekeh Pilaf (leftover from Day 1) and a green salad with Lemon Herb Vinaigrette (page 101)

Snack: (Serves 1) 1 cup melon

HERB-BAKED FISH (SERVES 4)

Keep this simple recipe in your back pocket for times when you need dinner in a pinch.

- **1 pound fresh fish (such as halibut, cod, or salmon)**
- **2 teaspoons olive oil**
- **1 teaspoon dried thyme**
- **¼ cup grated Parmigiano-Reggiano**

Preheat the oven to 425°F. Place the fish in a flat, oiled baking dish, skin-side down. Rub the top with olive oil, then sprinkle with the thyme and cheese. Bake for 10 minutes, or until the fish flakes easily with a fork. Serve immediately.

TABBOULEH—FOR DAY 3 (SERVES 2)

This recipe is easy to prepare ahead of time, making lunch the next day quick and simple to throw together. Prepare this on Day 2 and set it aside to enjoy with lunch on Day 3.

- ½ cup cooked bulgur
- 1 tablespoon lemon juice
- 1 clove garlic, minced
- 1 cup chopped parsley
- ¼ cup chopped mint
- 1 medium tomato, chopped
- Salt and pepper, to taste

Combine the warm cooked bulgur, lemon juice, and garlic and chill for 30 minutes. Add the remaining ingredients and season with salt and pepper to taste.

Day 3

Breakfast: Veggie Omelet with Farro (recipe follows) served with 1 kiwifruit per person, or 1-2-3 Breakfast of your choice (see page 4)

Lunch: Leftover Herb Baked Fish (from Day 2) served with 1 cup Tabbouleh (store-bought or homemade—page 33), or:

(Serves 1) 1 cup Tabbouleh (store-bought or homemade—page 33) served with ¼ cup hummus, 1 small whole wheat pita, 3 olives, ½ cup cucumber slices, and 1 clementine

Dinner: Mediterranean Pita Pizza (recipe follows) served with a simple salad of mixed greens, Balsamic Vinaigrette (page 101), ¼ cup cooked chickpeas, ¼ cup diced cucumber, and ¼ cup cherry tomatoes per person

Snack: ((Serves 1) 4 fresh figs

VEGGIE OMELET WITH FARRO (SERVES 2)

Farro adds a nutty flavor and texture to omelets. You may want to cook extra farro to save for lunch on Day 5. Freekeh is a wonderful substitute in this recipe if you don't have farro.

- **1 tablespoon olive oil**
- **1 small zucchini, diced**
- **1 red bell pepper, diced**
- **¼ cup cooked farro**
- **1 teaspoon dried tarragon**
- **2 eggs**
- **1 teaspoon water**

Heat the olive oil in a small skillet. Add the zucchini and pepper and sauté over medium-low heat for about 5 minutes, until the vegetables soften. Turn the heat up to medium-high and cook for a few minutes until the liquid in the pan evaporates, then add the farro. Combine the tarragon, eggs, and water in a small bowl and beat until smooth. Pour the eggs into the pan over the vegetables, reduce the heat to medium low, and cook until the edges of the omelet are set. Gently run a spatula under the eggs, lift up and tilt the pan to let some of the uncooked egg run into the bottom. Continue cooking for about 3 minutes longer, until the eggs are set.

MEDITERRANEAN PITA PIZZA (SERVES 4)

Be creative in choosing vegetable toppings: red, orange, or yellow peppers, thinly sliced onions or carrots, sliced spinach (add it under the cheese or on top after the pizza comes out of the oven), chopped artichoke hearts, or left-over veggies from last night's dinner.

- 4 large (8") whole grain pitas
- 1 cup tomato sauce
- ¼ cup (4 ounces) shredded mozzarella cheese
- 4 cups sliced mixed vegetables (such as mushrooms, peppers, broccoli, onions, etc.)
- 4 teaspoons olive oil

Preheat the oven to 350°F. Arrange the pita rounds on two baking sheets. Using the back of a spoon, spread about ¼ cup of tomato sauce evenly on top of each pita. Top each pizza with some grated cheese. Arrange your choice of vegetables on the top, then drizzle with olive oil. Bake for 15–20 minutes, until cheese is lightly browned.

Day 4

> Breakfast: (Serves 1) ½ cup low-fat plain Greek yogurt topped with 4 dried apricots and ¼ cup granola, or 1-2-3 Breakfast of your choice (see page 4)
>
> Lunch: Leftover Mediterranean Pita Pizzas (from Day 3), or:
>
> Slow Cooker Greek-Style Gigante Beans (recipe follows) served with crusty whole grain bread or a small, toasted whole wheat pita, and ½ cup broccoli roasted in olive oil
>
> Dinner: Whole Grain Pasta with Sardines and Swiss Chard (recipe follows))
>
> Snack: (Serves 1) 1 pear and 2 tablespoons almonds

SLOW COOKER GREEK GIGANTE BEANS (SERVES 4)

Look for bags of large white dried beans at any store that sells Mediterranean foods. Allow at least eight hours to soak the beans. Once they're cooked, freeze some for a meal down the road.

- 12 ounces dry gigante beans
- 1 (28-ounce) can chopped tomatoes, with juice
- 2 stalks celery, diced
- 1 onion, diced
- 4 cloves garlic, minced
- Water, as needed
- Salt, to taste

Put the beans in a large bowl, cover with water, and soak for eight hours or overnight. Drain, rinse, and add to a slow cooker with the remaining ingredients. Stir, and add a little water to cover the beans completely with liquid. Cover, and cook for 8 to 10 hours on low, until the beans are soft and tasty. Season to taste with salt (we use about 1 teaspoon of salt). Enjoy hot, at room temperature, or cold.

Week One: Mediterranean Diet

WHOLE GRAIN PASTA WITH SARDINES AND SWISS CHARD
(SERVES 4)

Because of the lively flavors of other ingredients, the sardines in this dish do not taste overly fishy.

- 12 ounces whole grain pasta, any shape
- 1 tablespoon plus 1 teaspoon olive oil, divided
- 2 cloves garlic, minced
- 1 bunch Swiss chard, chopped
- 2 cans wild sardines, spines removed and chopped
- 1 tablespoon capers

- 1 cup grape tomatoes, halved
- ⅛ teaspoon salt
- ¼ teaspoon pepper
- 1 teaspoon red chili flakes, plus more for serving
- 1 teaspoon lemon zest
- 1 tablespoon fresh parsley, chopped

Bring a pot of water to a boil. Add pasta and cook according to package instructions. While pasta is cooking, add 1 tablespoon olive oil to a deep saucepan and bring heat to medium. Add garlic and sauté until fragrant. Add Swiss chard and sauté until the leaves are soft. Add sardines, capers, grape tomatoes, salt, pepper, and chili flakes. Mix in the pan. When pasta is cooked to al dente, remove from heat and drain. Add the pasta to the pan with other ingredients, plus 1 teaspoon olive oil. Mix. Add lemon zest, fresh parsley, and extra red-chili flakes, if desired.

Day 5

Breakfast: (Serves 1) 1 cup cooked oatmeal topped with cinnamon, 1 diced peach, and 2 tablespoons part-skim ricotta, or 1-2-3 Breakfast of your choice (see page 4)

Lunch: Leftover Whole Grain Pasta with Sardines and Swiss Chard (from Day 4), or:

Pasta e Fagioli Soup (store-bought or homemade, recipe follows) served with a salad of mixed greens with ½ apple, thinly sliced, ¼ cup cooked farro (use the extra cooked at breakfast on Day 3), 1 tablespoon grated Parmigiano-Reggiano, and Balsamic Vinaigrette (page 101)

Dinner: Mediterranean Eggplant and Barley Salad (recipe follows), served with 4 ounces of grilled chicken per person

Snack: (Serves 1) 1 apple served with 1 tablespoon peanut butter

PASTA E FAGIOLI (SERVES 4)

This traditional Italian soup is very hearty and satisfying, loaded with pasta, beans, and vegetables.

- 1 tablespoon olive oil
- ¼ teaspoon dried rosemary
- ¼ teaspoon dried thyme
- 1 dried bay leaf
- 1 small onion, finely chopped
- 1 small carrot, finely chopped
- 1 rib celery, finely chopped
- 2 large cloves garlic, minced
- 1 (14.5-ounce) can white beans
- ½ cup canned tomato sauce or canned crushed tomatoes
- 1 cup water
- 2 cups low-sodium chicken stock
- 3 ounces small whole grain pasta
- Salt and pepper, to taste
- Optional: Grated Parmigiano-Reggiano or Romano cheese

Warm oil in a stock pot over medium-high heat. Add herbs, bay leaf, onion, chopped vegetables, garlic, and stir. Add the beans, tomato sauce, water, and stock to pot and raise the heat to high. Bring soup to a rapid boil and add the pasta. Reduce heat to

medium and cook soup, stirring occasionally, 6 to 8 minutes or until pasta is cooked al dente. Taste and adjust seasoning. Remove the bay leaf from soup after turning off heat. Serve with freshly grated cheese on top.

MEDITERRANEAN EGGPLANT AND BARLEY SALAD (SERVES 6)

Serve cold or at room temperature, with spicy greens such as arugula.

- 1 large eggplant, diced
- 2 medium zucchini, diced
- 2 tablespoons olive oil, divided
- Pinch of salt and pepper
- 1 bunch scallions, chopped
- 1½ teaspoons ground cumin
- ½ teaspoon ground coriander
- ¼ teaspoon cayenne
- 1 cup whole grain barley
- 3 cups water
- Juice of 1 lemon

- 2 cloves garlic, minced
- 1 teaspoon za'atar
- ½ pound cherry tomatoes, quartered
- ⅓ cup Kalamata olives, pitted and halved
- 1 (14.5-ounce) can white beans, drained and rinsed
- 1 cup fresh flat-leaf parsley, chopped
- ½ cup chopped fresh mint
- 3 cups fresh arugula

Preheat the oven to 425°F. Toss the eggplant and zucchini in a bowl with 1 tablespoon of the oil, salt, and pepper. Spread in a lightly greased baking pan and roast, until golden brown, about 20 minutes. Cool. While the vegetables are roasting, heat the remaining 1 tablespoon of oil in a large pot over medium-high heat. Add the scallions, cumin, coriander, and cayenne, and cook, stirring, until fragrant, about 1 minute. Add the barley and cook, stirring, for 2 minutes more. Add the water and bring to a boil. Reduce the heat and simmer, covered, for 40 minutes, or until almost all of the liquid is absorbed and the barley is tender. Remove from the heat and let stand, covered, for 15 minutes to allow the barley to absorb any additional liquid. Whisk together the lemon juice, garlic, and za'atar in a large bowl. Add the barley, roasted vegetables, tomatoes, olives, beans, parsley, and mint to the bowl and toss to combine. Toss with arugula just before serving.

Day 6

Breakfast: (Serves 1) 2 slices whole grain toast topped with 2 tablespoons part-skim ricotta and ¼ cup fresh blueberries, 1-2-3 Breakfast of your choice (see page 4)

Lunch: Leftover Mediterranean Eggplant and Barley Salad (from Day 5) served with 4 ounces of grilled chicken per person, or:

Avocado Tuna Salad in a Pita Pocket (recipe follows)

Dinner: Steel Cut Oat Risotto with Mushrooms (recipe follows) served with 4 ounces seared fish and 5 roasted asparagus spears per person

Snack: (Serves 1) ½ cup whole-grain crackers served with ½ avocado, mashed

AVOCADO TUNA SALAD IN A PITA POCKET (SERVES 4)

This lunchbox classic gets a Mediterranean makeover with Greek yogurt, tomatoes, and fresh herbs.

- 1 ripe avocado
- ¼ cup plain Greek yogurt
- 1 clove garlic, minced
- ¼ teaspoon salt
- ¼ teaspoon ground black pepper
- 2 tablespoons fresh dill, chopped

- 2 (4-ounce) cans tuna
- 1 small red onion, finely chopped
- Juice from ½ lemon
- ⅓ cup cherry tomatoes, halved
- 4 small whole wheat pitas, halved
- 1 cup fresh arugula

In a medium bowl, mash the avocado and Greek yogurt until smooth. Then add the garlic, salt, pepper, dill, tuna, onion and lemon juice and stir until well combined. Gently fold in the tomato halves, and stuff each pita pocket with the tuna salad and a handful of fresh arugula.

Week One: Mediterranean Diet

STEEL CUT OAT RISOTTO WITH MUSHROOMS (SERVES 4)

Unlike some grains, which must be furiously stirred into submission to create risotto, steel cut oats give up their creaminess almost willingly, making them an ideal star for whole grain risotto.

- 3 cups low-sodium vegetable broth
- ½ cup white wine
- 1 tablespoon olive oil
- 1 small onion, chopped
- 2 cloves garlic, minced
- 1½ cups white (button) mushrooms, sliced
- 1 cup steel cut oats (uncooked)
- Salt and pepper, to taste
- 2 tablespoons fresh sage, chopped

Heat the broth and wine in a small pot over low-medium heat until warm, but not boiling. While the broth mixture is warming, heat the oil in a large pot over medium heat, then add the onions and cook for about 3 minutes, stirring occasionally. Add the garlic and mushrooms to the onions and cook for an additional minute. Stir the oats into the vegetable mixture, and add ½ cup of the warm broth mixture into the pot. Stir frequently over medium heat until all of the moisture is absorbed. Repeat, adding ½ cup of the broth mixture at a time, until all of the broth mixture is used, and the oats reach a creamy consistency (approximately 20–25 minutes). Taste and adjust seasonings. Then, divide the risotto into four bowls, and garnish with fresh sage.

Day 7

Breakfast: (Serves 1) 2 slices whole grain toast topped with ½ avocado, mashed, ¼ cup arugula, and 2 ounces of smoked salmon, served with ½ cup fresh berries,, or 1-2-3 Breakfast of your choice (see page 4)

Lunch: Leftover Steel Cut Oat Risotto with Mushrooms (from Day 6) served with arugula salad tossed with chickpeas (1/2 cup per person) and Lemon Herb Vinaigrette (page 101), or:

Salad (serves 1) 1 cup arugula, ½ cup cooked farro, 3 dates, chopped, 2 tablespoons dried cranberries, 2 tablespoons almonds, 1 ounce of grated Parmigiano-Reggiano, and 2 tablespoons Lemon Herb Vinaigrette (page 101)

Dinner: Spaghetti with Mussels and Tomato Sauce (recipe follows) served with ½ cup roasted broccoli, lightly sprinkled with grated Parmesan, and mixed greens with Lemon Herb Vinaigrette (page 101)

Snack: (Serves 1) 1 cup grapes

SPAGHETTI WITH MUSSELS AND TOMATO SAUCE (SERVES 4)

Mussels should be rinsed, and lightly scrubbed if necessary, to remove any debris. Most farm-raised mussels come debearded, meaning that the thin, sticky membranes near the seam of the mussel have been removed. If there are any stubborn beards remaining, simply pull them off.

- 10 ounces whole grain spaghetti
- 2 tablespoons olive oil
- 1 small onion, chopped
- 3 cloves garlic, minced
- 2 (14.5-ounce) cans of diced tomatoes
- ¼ cup fresh basil, chopped, for garnish
- Salt and pepper, to taste
- 2 pounds mussels, cleaned and debearded (see note above)
- 2 ounces Parmigiano-Reggiano, grated

Week One: Mediterranean Diet

Bring a large pot of water to a boil, then add spaghetti. Cook according to package instructions (approximately 8 minutes), drain, and divide between four bowls. While the pasta is cooking, heat the olive oil in a small pan over medium heat. Add the onion and sauté for approximately four minutes. Then add the garlic and sauté for an additional four minutes, or until onions are translucent. Transfer the onion mixture to a blender, along with the 2 cans of tomatoes, and blend until well combined, but still a bit chunky (or until the mixture reaches the desired texture). Pour the tomato sauce into a large stock pot and heat over a medium-high heat until bubbly. Season with salt and pepper to taste. Add mussels to the pot and steam until shells open, about 5 minutes. Divide the cooked mussels between the four bowls of spaghetti and top with tomato sauce, grated Parmigiano-Reggiano, and fresh basil.

Mediterranean Eggplant and Barley Salad

(recipe pg.39)

Whole Grain Pasta with Sardines and Swiss Chard

(recipe pg.37)

African Heritage Diet Pyramid

Occasionally

Sweets

Moderate Portions
Daily to Weekly

Dairy

Drink Water

Eggs, Poultry & Other Meats **Healthy Oils**

Often, At Least
Two Times
Per Week

Fish & Seafood

Herbs, Spices, and Traditional Sauces

Whole Grains

Base Every
Meal On
These
Foods

Black Beans

Beans & Peas

Peanuts & Nuts

Fruits **Vegetables** **Tubers**

Greens

Enjoy
A Healthy
Lifestyle

Be Physically Active; Enjoy Meals With Others

Day 8

Breakfast: (Serves 1) 1 cup whole grain corn grits, topped with 1 sliced banana and a scrambled egg, or 1-2-3 Breakfast of your choice (see page 4)

Lunch: Leftover Spaghetti with Mussels and Tomato Sauce (from Day 7), served with ½ cup roasted zucchini, or:

Millet with Zucchini and Chickpeas (recipe follows) served with a salad of spinach with ¼ cup chopped walnuts and Herb Vinaigrette (page 101).

Dinner: Herb-Crusted Tilapia and Garlicy Dill Greens (recipe follows) with ⅔ cup of cooked brown rice

Snack: (Serves 1) 1 cup of grapes

MILLET WITH ZUCCHINI AND CHICKPEAS (SERVES 4)

The millet in this dish becomes very creamy—the perfect comfort food for a rainy day. Cook a little extra millet and save for breakfast on Day 9.

- 2 tablespoons olive oil, divided
- 1 large zucchini, diced
- Salt and pepper, to taste
- 1 large yellow onion, diced
- 3 cloves garlic, minced
- 1 cup dried millet

- 3½ cups water
- 1 teaspoon curry powder
- 1 (14.5-ounce) can of chickpeas, no salt added, rinsed and drained
- ¼ cup golden raisins (optional)

In a medium-sized pot, heat one tablespoon of olive oil on medium heat. Add zucchini with salt and pepper, stirring occasionally. Sauté for 4–5 minutes, or until vegetable softens. Remove zucchini from the pot and set aside. In the same pot, heat one tablespoon of olive oil over medium heat. Add onions and garlic and sauté for 4–5 minutes, or until onions are translucent. Add millet to the pot and toast for 2–3 minutes, stirring occasionally. Add water and curry powder. Bring to a boil, then simmer on low, covered, for 15 to 20 minutes. When millet is softened, turn off heat and allow to sit for 5 minutes. Fluff with fork before adding zucchini, chickpeas, and raisins.

Week Two: African Heritage Diet

HERB-CRUSTED TILAPIA AND GARLICKY DILL GREENS (SERVES 6)

Leftover fish is great the next day over a salad or rolled in a wrap with hummus and your favorite vegetables.

For the fish

- 1 cup crushed whole grain breadcrumbs
- 1 cup spinach, minced
- 2 tablespoons salt-free all-purpose seasoning (or salad seasoning)
- 2 tablespoons olive oil
- 6 tilapia fillets (2 ½ pounds)
- Salt and pepper, to taste

For the greens

- 3 small bunches of greens (kale, chard, spinach, etc.), chopped
- 2 tablespoons olive oil, divided
- 1 cup milk
- 1 large clove garlic, minced
- Juice of ½ medium-sized lemon
- ½ teaspoon Dijon or spicy mustard
- ⅓ cup fresh dill, chopped (6–8 sprigs)
- Salt, to taste

Preheat the oven to 400°F. Toast crumbs over medium-high heat in a hot skillet, moving it constantly to prevent burning. When crumbs are golden brown, turn off the heat and set crumbs aside. Mix spinach, all-purpose seasoning, and toasted crumbs in a bowl. Pour the olive oil in a small bowl and put the fish fillets on a lined baking sheet. Brush each fillet with olive oil. Spoon the spinach mixture on top of each fillet, spreading and pressing gently as you go. Season with salt and pepper and bake for 10–15 minutes. Meanwhile, in a large frying pan, sauté the chopped greens in 1 tablespoon of olive oil for 3–5 minutes, until they have wilted and become bright green. Mix all of the remaining ingredients in a small bowl with a whisk. Pour over cooked greens. Remove fish from the oven when it flakes easily with a fork and serve with greens and brown rice.

Breakfast: (Serves 1) Warm smoothie: in a blender combine ½ banana, ½ peach, 1 date, 2 tablespoons cashews (soaked overnight), juice of one lime, ½ cup of orange juice and ½ cup of warm millet (if you're using leftover millet from Day 8, simply warm in a microwave), or 1-2-3 Breakfast of your choice (see page 4)

Lunch: Leftover Herb-Crusted Tilapia (from Day 8) served over salad greens or baby spinach with a side of ½ cup green beans roasted in olive oil per serving, or:

Black-Eyed Pea Salad Wrap (recipe follows)

Dinner: 4-ounce baked salmon fillet per person, Quinoa with Ginger and Carrots (recipe follows), and ½ cup roasted broccoli per servinge

Snack: (Serves 1) 1 cup pineapple

BLACK-EYED PEA SALAD WRAP (SERVES 6)

This recipe's vinaigrette is a medley of tangy, sweet and spicy flavors that really pull this wrap together. You can also use the dressing over salad or drizzled on any cooked whole grain.

- **2 (14.5-ounce) cans of black-eyed peas, rinsed and drained**
- **1 cup cucumber, diced**
- **1 cup red bell pepper, diced**
- **2 tablespoons jalapeño, diced and de-seeded (optional)**
- **2 tablespoons cilantro, chopped**
- **⅓ cup Dijon Vinaigrette (page 102)**
- **6 whole wheat wraps**

In a large bowl, combine the black-eyed peas, cucumber, peppers and cilantro. Add the vinaigrette to the black-eyed pea mixture, stirring to combine. Refrigerate to chill. When ready to eat, fill a whole wheat wrap with the salad filling, and roll it up.

Week Two: African Heritage Diet

QUINOA WITH GINGER AND CARROTS (SERVES 4)

Try this dish warm, at room temperature, or chilled over fresh greens.

- 1 tablespoon olive oil
- 3 cloves garlic, minced
- 2 large carrots, finely diced
- 1 tablespoon ginger root, minced
- 1½ cups uncooked quinoa
- 3 cups water
- Salt, to taste

Heat olive oil in a pan over medium heat. Add garlic, carrots, and ginger, and cook over medium heat for 3 minutes. Add the quinoa and water to the pot and bring to a boil. Cover and simmer over low heat for 20 minutes. Uncover, fluff with a fork, and season to taste.

Breakfast: (Serves 1) 2 slices of whole grain toast with ½ avocado, mashed and 2 slices of tomato, served with 6 ounces of yogurt, or 1-2-3 Breakfast of your choice (see page 4)

Lunch: (Serves 1) 1 whole wheat wrap filled with leftover Quinoa with Ginger and Carrots (from Day 9) or Cabbage and Carrot Slaw (page 101) and avocado slices, served with ½ cup mixed raisins and peanuts

Dinner: Curried Couscous with Peppers (recipe follows) and Tangy Collard Greens (recipe follows)

Snack: (Serves 1) 1 mangos

CURRIED COUSCOUS WITH PEPPERS (SERVES 4)

Whole wheat couscous is a small, grain-shaped pasta that cooks very quickly. While we love its chewy texture in this dish, you could easily use bulgur, barley, or sorghum as a substitute.

- 1 tablespoon olive oil
- 3 cloves garlic, minced
- 1 large red bell pepper, diced
- 1 (14.5-ounce) can chickpeas, drained and rinsed
- 1 tablespoon curry powder
- 1½ cups whole wheat couscous
- 2¼ cups water
- Salt, to taste

Heat olive oil in pan over medium heat. Add the garlic, pepper, chickpeas, and curry powder, and cook on medium-high heat for 3 minutes. Add the water and bring to a boil. Add the couscous, cover the pot with a lid, and simmer over low heat for 5 minutes. Uncover, fluff with a fork and season to taste.

Week Two: African Heritage Diet

TANGY COLLARD GREENS (SERVES 4)

This is an easy go-to side dish that really highlights the delicious flavor of greens. Try it with spinach, Swiss chard, or mustard greens, as well.

- 2 bunches collard greens
- 1 tablespoon olive oil
- 1 medium yellow onion, chopped
- 4 cloves garlic, minced
- 1 tablespoon Dijon mustard
- Juice of ¼ lemon
- Salt, to taste

Cut the collard greens into long, thin strips (roll up 1 bunch of collard leaves together like a tight tortilla; position the bunch horizontally, and cut into strips). Heat olive oil in a pan over medium heat. Add the onions and garlic, and cook for 2–3 minutes, until the onions are golden. Stir in the mustard and drizzle in the lemon juice. Add collards and toss with a spoon to coat. Add a pinch of salt and a couple of splashes of water to give the greens some moisture. Cover and cook for about 10–12 minutes. until collards turn bright green.

Day 11

Breakfast: Quinoa Porridge with Figs and Honey (recipe follows), or 1-2-3 Breakfast of your choice (see page 4)

Lunch: Leftover Curried Couscous with Peppers and Tangy Collard Greens (from Day 10), or:

(Serves 1) **Chilled Sorghum Salad**: ¾ cup cooked sorghum, 2 ounces cooked chicken breast, diced, ¼ cup chopped cucumber, ¼ cup chopped tomatoes, fresh chopped herbs (try oregano or mint), 2 tablespoons extra-virgin olive oil and 1 tablespoon lemon juice for dressing

Dinner: Jollof Rice (recipe follows), served with 1 cup assorted sautéed greens (kale, collards, mustard greens, etc.) tossed with ½ cup black-eyed peas, 2 tablespoons lemon juice, and ¼ teaspoon paprika

Snack: (Serves 1) 1 cup watermelon

QUINOA PORRIDGE WITH FIGS AND HONEY (SERVES 4)

This sweet, creamy porridge is sure to warm you up on a cold winter morning. If you want to get a jump start on Day 13's breakfast, cook some extra quinoa in a separate pan at the same time and refrigerate for later.

- **1 cup white quinoa**
- **2 cups water**
- **½ teaspoon ground cinnamon**
- **¼ teaspoon ground cloves**
- **1 cup sliced dried figs**
- **1 cup chopped walnuts, toasted**
- **1 cup milk**
- **Honey, to taste**

Rinse the quinoa under cold water. In a medium sauce pan over medium heat, add the quinoa, water, cinnamon, and cloves, and bring to a boil. Reduce heat and cover, allowing quinoa to simmer for about 10 to 15 minutes, or until the water is absorbed and the grain is tender. Fluff the quinoa with a fork. Stir in the dried figs, nuts, milk and honey. Let sit for 5 minutes before serving to allow the flavors to meld, and the fruit to soften.

Week Two: African Heritage Diet

JOLLOF RICE (SERVES 4)

This dish is an African Heritage classic with West African roots.

- 1 (14.5-ounce) can diced tomatoes, drained (save liquid)
- 3 cups liquid (see below)
- 1½ cups uncooked brown rice
- 2 tablespoons olive oil
- 1 large onion, chopped (about 2 cups)
- 2–3 cloves garlic, minced
- 1 large carrot, chopped (about 1 cup)
- ¼ head of green cabbage, chopped (about 2 cups)
- 2 tablespoons tomato paste
- 1 teaspoon turmeric
- 1 teaspoon thyme
- ½ teaspoon red pepper flakes

Drain liquid from the diced tomatoes into a measuring cup. Add enough water to equal 3 cups of liquid in total, and put in a medium-sized pot with the brown rice. Bring to a boil, then cover and simmer until rice is tender to your taste, about 30–35 minutes. While rice cooks, heat olive oil in a large pan. Cook the onion and garlic until the onion is soft and translucent, about 5 minutes. Add chopped carrots and cabbage, tomato paste, canned tomatoes, and spices. Cover pan and simmer for a few minutes on low heat until the vegetables are done to your taste. When the rice is done, mix with the vegetables and serve.

Day 12

Breakfast: (Serves 1) 2 slices whole grain toast topped with ½ avocado, mashed, ¼ cup spinach and ¼ cup mashed chickpeas, served with ½ cup fresh berries, or 1-2-3 Breakfast of your choice (see page 4)

Lunch: Leftover Jollof Rice (from Day 11), served with a green salad, or:

Spinach Cucumber Dill Salad (recipe follows) and one slice of whole grain toast with 1 tablespoon peanut butter per serving

Dinner: Moroccan Tagine with Prunes (recipe follows) served with ½ cup whole wheat couscous or 1 slice whole wheat bread per person

Snack: (Serves 1) ½ cup of dried apricots

SPINACH CUCUMBER DILL SALAD (SERVES 4)

Add some cooked chicken or a hard-boiled egg and put it in a whole wheat wrap for an easy, on-the-go lunch.

- 2 cups spinach (9-ounce bag or 1 bunch of loose)
- 3 cucumbers, halved and thinly sliced
- 5 sprigs of fresh dill
- 5 large basil leaves, chopped
- 1 tablespoon apple-cider vinegar
- 2 tablespoons olive oil
- Juice of ¼ lemon
- Salt and pepper, to taste
- 3 avocados, sliced or chopped

Rinse greens and dry with a towel, then chop into smaller pieces. Mix the cucumber and spinach together in a bowl. Pull the dill leaves from their stalks, mince finely, and add with basil to the salad. Drizzle vinegar, oil, and lemon juice into the bowl, and add a pinch of salt and pepper. Toss to coat. Top with slices of avocado.

Week Two: African Heritage Diet

MOROCCAN TAGINE WITH PRUNES (SERVES 6)

Traditionally, this dish is cooked in a special, earthenware pot with a conical lid, called a tagine. Cooking the meal slowly, over low heat keeps the meat very tender and juicy and allows all the flavors to blend and almost melt together.

- 1 teaspoon each (ground): cinnamon, allspice, cardamom, cloves, ginger, cayenne, aniseed, nutmeg, turmeric, paprika, and cumin
- 1 pound tender lamb or beef, cut into 1½ inch cubes
- ¼ cup olive oil, divided
- 1 large onion, finely chopped
- 3 cloves garlic, crushed
- 2 tablespoons chopped fresh cilantro

- 1 (14.5-ounce) can chickpeas, drained and rinsed
- 1 (14.5-ounce) can diced tomatoes
- 6 cups low-sodium vegetable stock, divided
- ½ cup pitted prunes
- 2 potatoes, chopped
- 2 carrots, sliced
- Salt, to taste
- ¼ cup halved almonds, toasted

Combine all of the spices. Drizzle the meat cubes with 2 tablespoons olive oil and toss with the spice mixture in a bowl. Cover with cling wrap and refrigerate for at least 10 hours. Heat the remaining olive oil (2 tablespoons) in a tagine or Dutch oven over medium heat. Sauté the meat for 5 minutes, until all sides are browned. Add onions, garlic, and cilantro and sauté until translucent, about 5 minutes more. Add chickpeas, tomatoes, and 4 cups of stock. Simmer on low heat for 40–50 minutes. Add prunes, potatoes, and carrots. Season to taste with salt. Stir in the rest of the stock. Cover and simmer for another 40–50 minutes or until the meat is cooked and tender. Garnish with the toasted almonds.

Day 13

Breakfast: (Serves 1) 2 scrambled eggs with ½ cup cooked quinoa (use extra from Day 11's breakfast, if saved), 1 chopped tomato, and ½ cup spinach, served with 1 orange, or 1-2-3 Breakfast of your choice (see page 4)

Lunch: Leftover Moroccan Tagine with Prunes (from Day 12), or:

African Peanut Soup (recipe follows) and whole grain crispbread or crackers

Dinner: Southern-Style Chicken and Wild Rice Pilaf (recipe follows) served with ½ cup Mango Papaya Salad (page 102) per person

Snack: (Serves 1) ½ cup whole grain crackers served with 2 tablespoons almond butter

AFRICAN PEANUT SOUP (SERVES 6)

Peanut butter in soup? Trust us, the creaminess of the peanut butter thickens this soup beautifully, and the addition of ginger and curry powder really make it sing.

- 1 tablespoon peanut oil
- 1 medium onion, chopped
- 2 celery ribs, chopped
- 1 medium carrot, chopped
- 1 tablespoon fresh ginger, minced
- 2 cloves garlic, minced
- 2 teaspoons curry powder
- 4 cups water
- 8 ounces sweet potatoes, cut into 1-inch pieces
- 1 (14.5-ounce) can no-salt-added diced tomatoes
- ½ cup creamy unsalted peanut butter
- 1 (14.5-ounce) can low-sodium white beans, drained and rinsed
- ⅓ cup light coconut milk
- ½ teaspoon salt

Heat oil in a Dutch oven over medium-high heat. Add the onion, celery, carrot, ginger, and garlic. Cook, stirring occasionally, until slightly softened, 4–5 minutes. Add the curry powder and cook, stirring, 30 seconds. Stir in the water, potatoes, and diced tomatoes. Bring to a boil, reduce the heat to medium and simmer, uncovered, 20 minutes. Whisk

in the peanut butter until smooth. Add the beans, cover, return to a simmer and cook 15 minutes. Stir in the coconut milk, cover, and cook 2 minutes longer. Remove from the heat and stir in the salt. Let the soup cool for 10 minutes. Transfer the soup to a blender in batches and puree. Return to the pot and warm over medium heat.

SOUTHERN-STYLE CHICKEN AND WILD RICE PILAF (SERVES 6)

Pair this delicious and healthy take on Southern Fried Chicken with wild rice pilaf. The wild rice maintains its firmness and has a wonderful, nutty aroma which works really well with the tart, sweetness of the cherries in this recipe.

- 1 cup wild rice
- 1 cup water
- 2 cups low-sodium vegetable stock
- ½ tablespoon unsalted butter
- ½ cup chopped pecans
- 1 cup cooked and shredded chicken
- ½ cup fresh parsley, finely chopped
- 2 cloves garlic, minced
- ⅔ cup dried cherries
- 1 tablespoon olive oil
- Pinch of red pepper flakes
- Salt and pepper, to taste

Rinse the wild rice until the water runs clear. Combine the wild rice, water, stock, and butter in a heavy, medium saucepan. Bring to a boil at medium-high heat. Turn the heat down to low, cover, and simmer for 40 minutes. Meanwhile, toast the pecans in a skillet over medium heat, moving around to keep them from burning. When the pecans have browned, remove them from the heat. Stir the chicken, parsley, garlic, dried cherries, and chopped pecans together in a large mixing bowl. When the rice has finished cooking, uncover and remove from heat. Let rest for 5 minutes before draining off any excess water. Stir in olive oil, red pepper flakes, and rice, and mix to combine. Season with salt and pepper.

Day 14

Breakfast: Maple Walnut Teff Porridge (recipe follows), or 1-2-3 Breakfast of your choice (see page 4)

Lunch: Leftover Southern-Style Chicken and Wild Rice Pilaf (from Day 13), or:

Caribbean Coconut Red Beans (recipe follows), served with ⅔ cup of cooked brown rice per person (cook extra rice and save for Day 16's burrito bowl lunch, if you like)

Dinner: (Serves 1) North-African-inspired mezze platter, choose 3 or 4 of the following: ¼ cup hummus, ¼ cup baba ghanoush, ¼ cup roasted red peppers, ¼ cup roasted tomatoes, ¼ cup roasted eggplant, 1 hard-boiled egg, 2 ounces sardines, ¼ cup olives, 1 piece whole grain pita bread.

Snack: (Serves 1) 1 apple

MAPLE WALNUT TEFF PORRIDGE (SERVES 4)

Teff, a staple in Ethiopia, Eritrea, and other countries in the Horn of Africa, is the smallest of all the grains—just 1/150 the size of wheat kernels. We enjoy its lovely, chocolatey undertones.

- 1½ cups water
- ½ cup coconut milk
- 1 cup teff (whole grain, not the flour)
- ½ teaspoon ground cardamom
- 1¼ teaspoon sea salt
- 1 tablespoon maple syrup
- ¼ cup chopped walnuts

In a medium pot, bring the water and coconut milk to a boil and add the teff. Quickly lower the heat to a simmer. Stir in the cardamom and sea salt and cook (uncovered) for 20 minutes, or until all the liquid is absorbed. Stir every 5 minutes or so to keep the mixture from sticking. When the teff is fully cooked, stir in the maple syrup and chopped walnuts to thoroughly incorporate.

CARIBBEAN COCONUT RED BEANS (SERVES 6)

This dish tastes even better the next day. Make some extra to have as leftovers for lunch on Day 15 .

- 6 cloves garlic, minced
- 1 teaspoon allspice
- 1 teaspoon dried thyme
- ½ (13.5-ounce) can light coconut milk
- 2 (14.5-ounce) cans of red beans, drained and rinsed
- Salt, to taste

Sauté the garlic with the allspice and thyme in the coconut milk for 3–4 minutes on medium heat. Stir in the beans and continue to cook over medium-low heat; cover and cook for 10 minutes. Season to taste.

Quinoa Porridge with Figs and Honey

(recipe pg.54)

Jollof Rice

(recipe pg.55)

Latin American Heritage Diet Pyramid

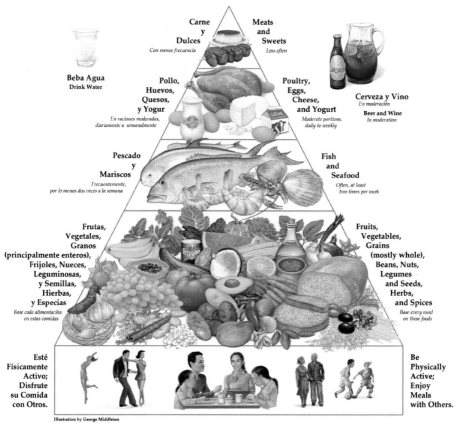

Carne y Dulces
Con menos frecuencia

Meats and Sweets
Less often

Beba Agua
Drink Water

Pollo, Huevos, Quesos, y Yogur
En raciones moderadas, diariamente a semanalmente

Poultry, Eggs, Cheese, and Yogurt
Moderate portions, daily to weekly

Cerveza y Vino
En moderación
Beer and Wine
In moderation

Pescado y Mariscos
Frecuentemente, por lo menos dos veces a la semana

Fish and Seafood
Often, at least two times per week

Frutas, Vegetales, Granos (principalmente enteros), Frijoles, Nueces, Leguminosas, y Semillas, Hierbas, y Especias
Base cada alimentación en estas comidas

Fruits, Vegetables, Grains (mostly whole), Beans, Nuts, Legumes and Seeds, Herbs, and Spices
Base every meal on these foods

Esté Físicamente Activo; Disfrute su Comida con Otros.

Be Physically Active; Enjoy Meals with Others.

Illustration by George Middleton

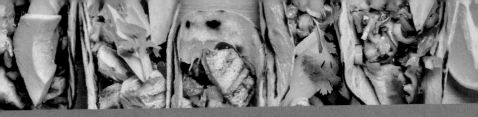

Day 15

FIESTA QUINOA SALAD (SERVES 4)

This recipe is flexible, so add or change the ingredients to your liking. Soybeans, tomatoes, sliced cooked chicken, or grilled steak are all possible options to swap in. Cook extra quinoa and reserve it to get a head start on the Stuffed Poblanos dinner recipe on Day 17.

- 1 cup quinoa
- 2 cups low-sodium vegetable broth
- 2 ears corn, roasted and cut off cob
- 1 red bell pepper, roasted and chopped
- 1 (14.5-ounce) can black beans, rinsed and drained
- 3 scallions, sliced

- ½ cup chopped cilantro
- Juice of 3 limes
- 2 tablespoons olive oil
- 1 teaspoon ground cumin
- ½ teaspoon salt
- ¼ teaspoon fresh ground black pepper
- ⅛ teaspoon cayenne pepper

Put quinoa and broth in a medium saucepan. Bring to a boil, cover, and simmer for 15 minutes or until tender. In a large bowl, mix together quinoa, corn, pepper, beans, scallions, and cilantro. In a small bowl, whisk together lime juice, olive oil and

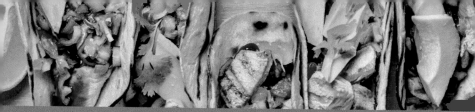

seasonings. Pour over quinoa mixture. Cover and chill for at least 30 minutes to let the flavors blend and set.

OLDWAYS WILD VEGGIE TOSTADAS (SERVES 4)

While we often make this recipe with brown rice, wild rice adds a beautiful texture and aroma to these zesty tostadas.

- 1 cup wild rice
- 2 teaspoons olive oil
- 1 medium red onion, sliced into half moons
- 3 cloves garlic, minced
- 1 large poblano pepper, or bell pepper, seeded and sliced
- ¼ head purple cabbage, shredded
- 1 bunch kale or chard, chopped
- Dash of salt
- 1 (14.5-ounce) can low-sodium refried pinto beans
- 8 flat, crispy whole grain corn "tostada" tortillas
- 1 avocado, peeled and sliced
- Salsa of your choice

In a small pot, prepare the wild rice according to the package instructions. While it's cooking, heat the oil in a large pan, and sauté the red onion, garlic, and pepper until soft and aromatic. Add the cabbage, kale, and a pinch of sea salt; cover the pan and let the veggies cook for 5–6 minutes, until they are soft. In another small pot, heat the refried beans. Add a dash of water, if necessary, to thin the beans for easier spreading. To assemble the tostadas, spread a large spoonful of beans evenly onto each tostada. Add one spoonful of wild rice and spread on top of the beans, then add the veggie medley, avocado slices, and top with salsa. Serve 2 tostadas per person.

Day 16

Breakfast: Oldways Easy Huevos Rancheros (recipe follows), or 1-2-3 Breakfast of your choice (see page 4)

Lunch: Leftover Oldways Wild Veggie Tostadas (from Day 15) served with a green salad, or:

"Burrito bowl" (Serves 1) with ½ cup chopped lettuce, ½ cup cooked whole grains (like quinoa, brown rice, or sorghum), ⅓ cup black or pinto beans, ½ avocado, Cilantro Lime Crema (page 102), and salsa of choice

Dinner: Fish Tacos with Mango Salsa (recipe follows)

Snack: (Serves 1) 1 cup fruit salad

OLDWAYS EASY HUEVOS RANCHEROS (SERVES 2)

Make extra batches of this spiced black bean dish, so that you can enjoy it for lunch the next day as a filling for tacos

For the spiced black beans

- 2 teaspoons extra-virgin olive oil, plus more for eggs
- 1 onion, chopped
- 1 bell pepper, chopped
- 1 (14.5-ounce) can black beans, drained and rinsed
- ¼ cup salsa

For serving

- 2 eggs
- ½ avocado, sliced
- 2 small corn or whole wheat tortillas, warmed

In a medium skillet, heat oil over medium heat, then add the onion and bell pepper and sauté until slightly translucent. Add the black beans and salsa and cook over medium-low heat, stirring occasionally, until warmed through. While the black beans are cooking, fry the eggs in olive oil in a separate pan or poach them. Divide the black bean mixture between two bowls, then top each bowl with an egg and avocado slices, and serve with a warm whole grain tortilla.

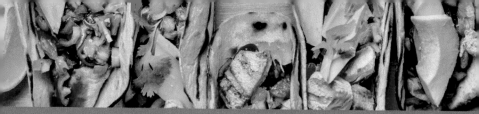

FISH TACOS WITH MANGO SALSA (SERVES 2)

This impressive dinner actually comes together quite quickly. Whole grain corn tortillas or whole wheat tortillas work equally well.

- 1 jalapeño pepper, seeded and diced
- 1 mango, diced
- ¼ cup cilantro, chopped
- Juice of 1 lime
- ¼ teaspoon chili powder
- ¼ teaspoon ground cumin
- ¼ teaspoon paprika
- ¼ teaspoon salt
- ½ pound fish
- 1 tablespoon extra-virgin olive oil
- 4 small whole grain tortillas
- ½ cup cabbage, thinly sliced
- 1 avocado, sliced
- ¼ cup plain Greek yogurt

Add the jalapeño, mango, cilantro, and lime juice to a small mixing bowl and stir until combined. In a very small bowl, combine the chili powder, cumin, paprika, and salt and stir. Evenly sprinkle this spice mixture over the fish fillets. Heat olive oil in a large skillet over medium high heat, and add fish fillets. Cook for 1–3 minutes (depending on the thickness). Then flip, and cook for an additional 1–3 minutes, until opaque. Divide the fish between the four tortillas. Top each fish taco with cabbage, mango salsa, avocado slices, and plain yogurt.

Day 17

Breakfast: "Mosh"—Guatemalan Oatmeal (recipe follows) served with 1 banana with 1 tablespoon almond butter per person, or 1-2-3 Breakfast of your choice (see page 4)

Lunch: (Serves 1) 2 whole grain wheat or corn tortillas filled with Spiced Black Beans (leftover from Huevos Rancheros recipe, on day 16), ½ avocado, sliced, and 2 tablespoons plain Greek yogurt, plus 4 slices unsweetened dried mango, or:

Quesadilla (serves 1) made with 1 ounce shredded Colby or Monteray Jack cheese, ¼ cup shredded chicken, and 1 red bell pepper, sliced, between 2 medium whole grain (whole wheat or corn) tortillas, served with a green salad topped with ½ avocado, sliced, and Lime Vinaigrette (page 102)

Dinner: Stuffed Poblanos (recipe follows) with Cilantro Lime Crema (page 102) served with a green salad with Lime Vinaigrette (page 102) and 1 orange

Snack: (Serves 1) Grilled pineapple slices with fresh mint

"MOSH" — GUATEMALAN OATMEAL (SERVES 4)

Mosh is a milky oatmeal dish served for breakfast in Guatemala and some other Central American countries. Unlike how it's prepared in the US, it is simmered for a long time with lots of liquid, making it drinkable. In this version, we use quick-cooking oats soaked overnight, so that breakfast cooks more quickly in the morning.

- ½ cup quick cooking oats
- 2½ cups milk, divided
- 1 teaspoons agave syrup or honey
- ¼ teaspoon cinnamon

Combine the oats and 2 cups of milk in a medium saucepan, then refrigerate, covered, overnight. In the morning, bring the mixture to a quick boil, then reduce heat to low and cook, stirring frequently, until creamy (about 15 minutes). When oatmeal reaches desired consistency (it should be drinkable), add the remaining ½ cup milk, agave and cinnamon, and stir over low heat for 1 more minute. Serve in 2 mugs.

STUFFED POBLANOS (SERVES 6)

We use quinoa in this recipe, but nearly any whole grain will do. Some of our other favorite pepper stuffings are amaranth, bulgur, and millet. If you saved quinoa from lunch on Day 15, just warm it in the microwave before incorporating it into this dish.

- 1 small butternut squash
- 6 poblano peppers
- 1 tablespoon olive oil
- ½ cup uncooked quinoa
- 1 (14.5-ounce) can black beans, drained and rinsed
- 1 cup corn kernels (can be fresh, canned, or frozen)

- 1 teaspoon smoked paprika
- 1 teaspoon ground cumin
- ¾ teaspoon salt
- ½ teaspoon pepper
- Cilantro Lime Crema (page 102)

Preheat oven to 450°F. Cut butternut squash in half lengthwise, remove seeds, and roast cut-side down for about 45–60 minutes until tender, then set aside to cool. Place the poblano peppers on a lined baking sheet and brush with olive oil. Roast for 10 minutes, until just tender. Remove from oven and let cool. Cook quinoa according to package directions. Scoop out the squash into a large bowl and mash it with a fork, then add the quinoa, black beans, corn, paprika, cumin, salt and pepper, and mix well. When poblanos are cooled, cut a slit lengthwise in each poblano, remove the seeds, then stuff them with the butternut squash mixture. Roast for an additional 10–15 minutes, until the top gets a bit crispy and browned. Top with Cilantro Lime Crema.

Day 18

Breakfast: Sauté 1 small new potato (diced) and 1 large husked tomatillo (diced) in extra-virgin olive oil, then scramble with 1 egg (beaten) and 1 tablespoon chopped green onions. Serve with 1 small whole grain tortilla and ½ cup papaya or melon, or 1-2-3 Breakfast of your choice (see page 4)

Lunch: Leftover Stuffed Poblanos (from Day 17) served with a green salad and 1 orange, or:

Amaranth with Peppers and Cabbage (recipe follows) served with 4 ounces roasted chicken per person

Dinner: Barley, Pineapple and Jicama Salad with Avocado (recipe follows) served with 4 ounces baked or grilled fish per person

Snack: ¼ cup guacamole (recipe on page 102) with ⅓ cup whole grain crackers or whole grain baked tortilla chips

AMARANTH WITH PEPPERS AND CABBAGE (SERVES 4)

This Latin American Heritage dish is a delicious way to use cabbage, one of our favorite winter vegetables. The mild heat from the poblano peppers perfectly complements the peppery amaranth grains, but feel free to substitute bell peppers, if you prefer them.

- 2 cups water
- 1 cup uncooked amaranth
- 2 cloves garlic, minced
- 1 green bell pepper, cored, seeded, and diced
- 1 poblano pepper, cored, seeded, and diced
- 2 tablespoons olive oil
- ¼ head purple cabbage, shredded
- Salt and pepper, to taste

To cook the amaranth, bring the water and amaranth to a boil, then simmer, partially covered, for 30–35 minutes, until soft, swollen, and tender. Remove from the heat and allow to stand for 15 minutes, with the lid still on, to swell more. Meanwhile, in a large shallow pan, gently fry the garlic and diced peppers in the oil until the vegetables are soft. Add the cabbage, season with salt and pepper, and put the lid on to cook for 5 more minutes. Gently stir in the amaranth grains, reheat and serve.

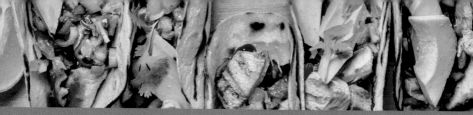

BARLEY, PINEAPPLE, AND JICAMA SALAD WITH AVOCADO (SERVES 6)

This fruity grain salad showcases the freshness of traditional Latin American cuisine. Cook extra barley to reserve for the South American Vegetable and Rice Soup on Day 19.

- 1 cup whole grain barley
- 3 cups water
- 2 tablespoons fresh lime juice
- ¼ cup olive oil
- ¼ teaspoon ground cumin
- ¼ teaspoon salt

- ¼ teaspoon ground black pepper
- 6 cups watercress or arugula
- 1 jicama root, peeled and grated
- 2 cups cubed pineapple (from about ½ medium pineapple)
- 2 large avocados, cubed

Bring barley and water to a boil, then reduce heat to a simmer and cook, covered, for 45–60 minutes, until the liquid is absorbed and the grains become tender. While the barley is cooking, whisk together the lime juice, olive oil, cumin, salt and pepper, then taste and adjust seasoning. In a large bowl, toss the watercress with half of the dressing. When barley is done cooking, drain off any excess liquid, then add the jicama, pineapple, avocado, and cooked barley to the watercress, along with the rest of the dressing, and toss gently to combine.

Day 19

Breakfast: Blend ½ cup plain Greek-style yogurt with ½ cup chopped mango, ½ frozen banana, and ¼ cup fresh spinach. Serve in a bowl and top with 2 tablespoons granola, or 1-2-3 Breakfast of your choice (see page 4)

Lunch: Leftover Barley, Pineapple and Jicama Salad with Avocado (from Day 18) served with 4 ounces baked or grilled fish per person, or:

South American Vegetable and Rice Soup (recipe follows) served with ⅓ cup whole grain tortilla chips or crackers and ⅓ cup refried beans or black bean dip per person

Dinner: Sautéed Quinoa with Swiss Chard (recipe follows) served with 4 ounces grilled chicken, fish or tofu and ½ cup fresh berries per perso

Snack: (Serves 1) ½ cup chopped jicama topped with juice of ½ lime and a pinch of chili powder

SOUTH AMERICAN VEGETABLE AND RICE SOUP (SERVES 4)

This soup recipe uses whole grain brown rice, but cooked barley, sorghum, or wheat berries would also be great. Use barley if you made extra at dinner on Day 18.

- ½ teaspoon olive oil
- 1 onion, chopped
- 4 cloves garlic, minced
- 1 teaspoon dried oregano
- ¼ teaspoon ground allspice
- ½ teaspoon ground cumin
- 4 cups low-sodium vegetable stock
- 4 fresh husked tomatillos (can substitute tomatoes)
- 1 (14.5-ounce) can diced tomatoes
- 1 cup canned black beans, drained and rinsed
- ½ cup corn kernels
- 1 medium zucchini, sliced into half moons
- ½ teaspoon chipotle pepper
- ¼ teaspoon salt
- 1 cup cooked brown rice (or another whole grain)
- 2 tablespoons chopped fresh cilantro (optional garnish)

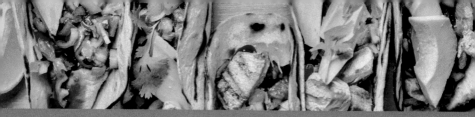

Heat the oil in a large saucepan over medium-high heat and cook the onion until it becomes translucent, about 2 minutes. Toss in the garlic, oregano, allspice and cumin, and cook for another 2 minutes, stirring so the garlic doesn't brown. Pour in the vegetable stock, the tomatillos, and the can of tomatoes. Bring to boil, turn the heat down, and allow it to simmer for 10 minutes. Add the beans, corn, squash, chipotle pepper, and salt. Bring back to a boil, turn down the heat, and simmer for 5 minutes. Add the cup of cooked brown rice (or leftover barley) to the soup for the last 4–5 minutes of cook-time. Garnish with cilantro, if desired.

SAUTÉED QUINOA WITH SWISS CHARD (SERVES 4)

Quinoa has a rich history in Latin American cuisine, as it was a staple of the Inca in the Andes.

- 1 cup quinoa, rinsed
- 2 cups water
- 1 tablespoon olive oil, divided
- 2 cloves garlic, finely minced
- ½ teaspoon ground cumin
- 1 small yellow onion, finely chopped
- ½ bunch Swiss chard, leaves coarsely chopped, stems halved lengthwise and then sliced
- 1 teaspoon salt
- ½ teaspoon freshly ground black pepper

Bring quinoa and water to a boil, then reduce the heat to a simmer and cook, covered, for about 10 minutes, until the water is absorbed and the quinoa sprouts a "tail." Heat ½ tablespoon olive oil over medium heat in a large skillet. Add the garlic, cumin, onions, Swiss chard stems, and cook until tender. Add the chopped Swiss chard leaves and cook, stirring until they wilt, about 1 minute. Remove from heat and stir in the cooked quinoa and remaining ½ tablespoon oil. Season with salt and pepper, and cook until it is heated thoroughly.

Day 20

Breakfast: (Serves 1) Mexican egg scramble: 2 scrambled eggs with 1 small plum tomato (diced), 1 small jalapeno pepper (seeded and diced), and 1 green onion (diced). Serve with 1 apple and 1 warm, whole grain tortilla per person, or 1-2-3 Breakfast of your choice (see page 4)

Lunch: Leftover Sautéed Quinoa with Swiss Chard (from Day 19) served with 4 ounces grilled chicken, fish, or tofu and ½ cup fresh berries per person, or:

1 cup cooked whole grain cornmeal polenta per person topped with Sofrito (page 103) , served with Beans and Greens (recipe follows)

Dinner: "Arroz Con Pollo"—Rice with Chicken (recipe follows) served with ½ cup zucchini roasted in olive oil

Snack: (Serves 1) 1 cup grapes

BEANS AND GREENS (SERVES 4)

This recipe is the perfect side dish for lunch, dinner, or even breakfast. For an extra pop of flavor, top each serving with a spoonful of Queso Cotija or crumbled feta cheese.

- 1 (14.5-ounce) can black beans, drained and rinsed
- 4 cups chopped curly kale, freshly washed
- 1 avocado, pit removed, peeled and chopped
- ½ teaspoon salt
- ¼ teaspoon ground black pepper

In a large skillet, add a splash of water to the black beans and cook over low heat. Add the kale to the top of the beans, then cover and let steam for 1–3 minutes. When the kale is lightly wilted, remove from heat, and stir in the avocado chunks until they are evenly distributed. Add salt and pepper, then taste, and adjust seasonings.

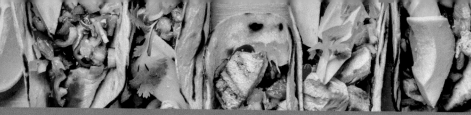

"ARROZ CON POLLO" — RICE WITH CHICKEN (SERVES 4)

Arroz con Pollo, Spanish for "rice with chicken," is a spin on the classic Spanish dish, paella.

- 2 tablespoons extra-virgin olive oil, divided
- 1 pound boneless skinless chicken pieces (breast or thighs, whichever you prefer)
- ½ cup Sofrito (page 103)
- ½ teaspoon ground cumin
- ¼ cup pitted olives, quartered
- 4 ounces tomato sauce (unsalted)
- 1 cup long-grain brown rice
- 2 cups water
- Salt and black pepper, to taste
- 2 tablespoons fresh thyme

In a large pot, heat the oil over medium heat. Brown the chicken on each side for approximately 5 minutes, then remove and set aside. Stir in the sofrito, cumin, olives and tomato sauce and cook for 4 minutes at low heat. Stir in the rice and chicken and mix well, then add water and bring to a boil. Reduce heat to a simmer and cook for 45 minutes, covered, until the internal temperature of the chicken reaches 165°F. Season with salt and pepper. Taste, adjust seasonings, then garnish with fresh thyme.

Day 21

Breakfast: Banana Amaranth Porridge (recipe follows), or 1-2-3 Breakfast of your choice (see page 4)

Lunch: Leftover "Arroz Con Pollo"–Rice with Chicken (from Day 20) and ½ cup zucchini roasted in olive oil, or:

Latin American Heritage plate (Serves 1) with ½ cup each refried pinto beans, spiced brown rice, corn, and sautéed leafy greens, and 2 tablespoons each Guacamole (page 102) and salsa

Dinner: Enchilada Casserole (recipe follows) served with ½ cup steamed green beans and ½ cup papaya slices per person

Snack: (Serves 1) ½ cup mixed dried plantains and cashews

BANANA AMARANTH PORRIDGE (SERVES 2)

Unlike rice or quinoa, which plump into individual kernels, the tiny amaranth grains cling together, making it well suited for warm polenta and porridge-inspired dishes.

- ½ cup amaranth
- 1½ cups milk
- 1 banana, sliced
- ¼ teaspoon dried ginger
- ½ teaspoon cinnamon
- 2 tablespoons cocoa nibs (optional)

In a small pot, bring amaranth and milk to a boil. Once boiling, reduce heat to a simmer, then add the banana slices and mash them into the porridge with a spoon. Simmer for 25 minutes, stirring occasionally, until the porridge thickens. Feel free to add more milk, to thin out as desired. Add ginger and cinnamon, then divide porridge into 2 bowls. Top with cocoa nibs, if desired.

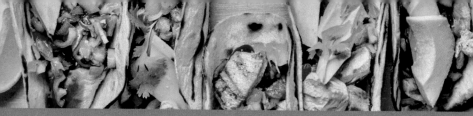

ENCHILADA CASSEROLE (SERVES 6)

....

This recipe is a family favorite.

- 1 teaspoon olive oil
- 1 (10-ounce) can green enchilada sauce, divided
- 6 small whole grain corn tortillas
- 1 (14.5-ounce) can black beans, drained and rinsed
- 1 large tomato, diced
- 2 cups packed baby spinach leaves

- 1 cup corn kernels (fresh, canned, or frozen)
- 5 scallions, chopped
- ⅓ cup fresh cilantro, chopped
- 1 cup Colby Jack cheese (or any melting semi-hard cow's milk cheese, like Fontina or raclette), shredded

Preheat oven to 375°F. Lightly oil a large baking dish, then speard half of the enchilada sauce on the bottom. Assemble the enchiladas on a flat work surface. Down the center of each tortilla, arrange about 3 tablespoons beans, 1 tablespoon tomato, ¼ cup spinach, 2 tablespoons corn, 1 tablespoon scallions, 2 teaspoons cilantro. Roll up tightly, burrito style, and place each enchilada, seam side down, on top of the sauce in the baking dish. Cover with the remaining enchilada sauce and sprinkle with the cheese and remaining scallions. Bake uncovered for 35 minutes, until golden brown.

Barley, Pineapple, and Jicama Salad with Avocado

(recipe pg.73)

"Arroz con Pollo"—Rice with Chicken

(recipe pg.77)

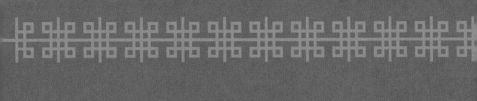

Asian Heritage Diet Pyramid

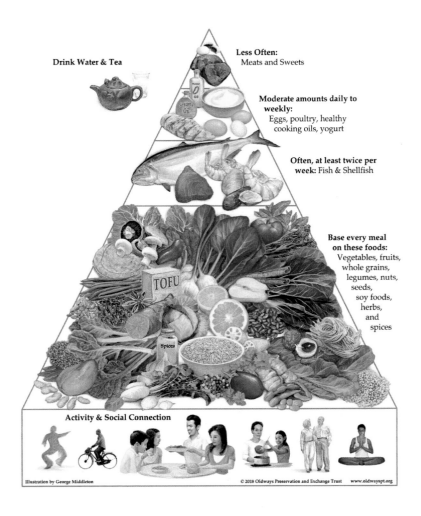

Drink Water & Tea

Less Often:
Meats and Sweets

Moderate amounts daily to weekly:
Eggs, poultry, healthy cooking oils, yogurt

Often, at least twice per week: Fish & Shellfish

Base every meal on these foods:
Vegetables, fruits, whole grains, legumes, nuts, seeds, soy foods, herbs, and spices

Activity & Social Connection

Illustration by George Middleton   © 2018 Oldways Preservation and Exchange Trust   www.oldwayspt.org

Day 22

Breakfast: (Serves 1) Creamy brown rice porridge: in a saucepan, combine ½ cup cooked brown rice, ½ cup milk, 1 teaspoon honey, and a pinch of cinnamon. Simmer 15 minutes until creamy and top with 1 chopped peach, or: 1-2-3 Breakfast of your choice (see page 4)

Lunch: Kimchi Soba Noodles (recipe follows) served with ¼ cup of Asian Trail Mix (page 104) per person, or:

Leftover Enchilada Casserole (from Day 21)

Dinner: Coconut Fish Curry with Mango and Sugar Snap Peas (recipe follows) with ⅔ cup of cooked brown rice per serving

Snack: (Serves 1) 1 pear

KIMCHI SOBA NOODLES (SERVES 6)

Kimchi is a staple in Korean cuisine, made by fermenting cabbage and other vegetables seasoned with garlic, ginger, and chilies. You can find it in the refrigerated section of most grocery stores.

- 1 pound dry buckwheat soba noodles
- 1 teaspoon peanut oil
- 2 cloves garlic, minced
- 1 cup mushrooms, sliced
- 6 scallions, thinly sliced
- 1 ¼ cups chopped kimchi
- 4 tablespoons sesame oil
- 3 tablespoons rice vinegar
- 3 tablespoons toasted sesame seeds

Fill a stockpot with water and bring to a boil, add soba noodles. Stir and cook, uncovered, for 5–10 minutes until al dente. Drain and rinse under cold water. While noodles are cooking, in a frying pan heat peanut oil over medium-high heat, add garlic and mushrooms. Cook for 6 minutes, or until mushrooms are tender. Remove from heat and cool. Place drained noodles into a large bowl and add cooked mushrooms, scallions, kimchi, sesame oil, and vinegar. Toss to combine. Top with toasted sesame seeds. Enjoy warm, room temperature, or chilled.

Week Four: Asian Heritage Diet

COCONUT FISH CURRY WITH MANGO AND SUGAR SNAP PEAS
(SERVES 4)

This is a summer favorite at Oldways. Fresh mango and crisp sugar snap peas make this dish as colorful as it is flavorful.

- 2 tablespoons extra-virgin olive oil
- 1 small onion, cut into ½-inch dice
- 2 cloves garlic, minced
- 1 jalapeño pepper, seeded and chopped
- 1 teaspoon grated fresh ginger
- 1 teaspoon curry powder
- ¼ teaspoon cayenne pepper

- 1 (14.5-ounce) can diced tomatoes
- 1 (14-ounce) can light coconut milk
- 8 ounces white fish (of your choosing), cut into bite-sized pieces
- 1 cup sugar snap peas, halved
- 1 mango, peeled, pitted, and diced
- ¼ teaspoon salt
- ¼ teaspoon pepper

Heat the oil in a large pot over medium heat. Add the onion, garlic, jalapeño pepper, ginger, curry powder, and cayenne pepper, and cook stirring frequently, until onions become translucent, about 10 minutes. Stir in the tomatoes and cook for an additional minute. Add the coconut milk and bring to a boil. Add the fish, sugar snap peas, mango, salt and pepper, and simmer for about 4 minutes, until the fish is cooked through. Ladle the curry into four bowls, over brown rice.

Day 23

Breakfast: (Serves 1) 1 cup plain Greek yogurt with 1 orange peeled into segments and chopped, and ¼ cup pistachios, served with 1 slice of whole grain toast, or: 1-2-3 Breakfast of your choice (see page 4)

Lunch: Leftover Coconut Fish Curry with Mango and Sugar Snap Peas (from Day 22), served with a green salad and 1 slice of whole grain bread, or:

Tom Yang Goong (recipe follows) served with ½ cup steamed edamame and ½ cup of whole grain crackers per person

Dinner: Black Rice Chicken Congee (recipe follows)

Snack: (Serves 1) 1 cup pineapple

TOM YANG GOONG (SERVES 4)

This traditional Thai dish is a spicy shrimp and mushroom soup dressed up with lemongrass.

- 6 cups low-sodium chicken or veggie stock
- 6 ounces button mushrooms, cut in half
- 1 tablespoon red chili paste
- 12 large raw shrimp, peeled and deveined
- 1 tablespoon fish sauce
- 2 red chilies, seeded and minced
- 2 tablespoons fresh lemongrass, minced
- 6 tablespoons fresh lime juice (juice of 2–3 limes)
- 4 tablespoons fresh cilantro, chopped

Bring the stock to a boil in a large saucepan, then lower the heat to a simmer. Add the mushrooms and chili paste and cook for 5 minutes. Bring the broth back to a full boil, and then add the shrimp, fish sauce, fresh chilies and lemongrass. Cook for two minutes, then remove from the heat, stir in the lime juice and cilantro.

Week Four: Asian Heritage Diet

BLACK RICE CHICKEN CONGEE (SERVES 2)

In ancient China, black rice (also called "forbidden rice") was reserved for royalty. Its lovely, dark color serves as a beautiful backdrop to the chicken, mushroom and scallions in this recipe. While some Asian congees are thin and soupy, this one cooks up more like risotto.

- 2 cloves garlic, minced
- 2 tablespoons fresh ginger, chopped
- 1 tablespoon sesame oil
- 2½ cups low-sodium chicken stock, divided
- ½ cup uncooked black rice
- 2 tablespoons extra-virgin olive oil
- 2 large boneless chicken thighs, dusted with whole wheat flour
- ¼ cup shiitake mushrooms, chopped
- 2 tablespoons peanuts, chopped
- 1 tablespoon low-sodium soy sauce
- 2 scallions, chopped
- Salt and black pepper, to taste

Blend the garlic, ginger, and sesame oil with a mortar and pestle into a paste. In a medium saucepan, bring 2 cups of the stock to a simmer. Add the black rice and simmer, covered, for 30 minutes. Remove from the heat and set aside. Heat a small frying pan over high heat, heat olive oil, and then add the chicken thighs. Cook for a few minutes on each side until a meat thermometer reads 165°F when inserted into the thickest part of the chicken, then remove from the heat. Place the meat on a clean cutting board, and shred it into small pieces. Reheat the frying pan, add a little olive oil, and add the mushrooms. Cook for 6 minutes, until they are tender. While the mushrooms are cooking, add the remaining ½ cup of broth and the garlic-ginger paste to the black rice and return to low heat, cooking for 10 minutes. Divide the rice into two bowls and top with mushrooms, chicken, peanuts, soy sauce, and scallions. Season with salt and pepper and serve.

Day 24

Breakfast: (Serves 1) 1 whole wheat naan or paratha filled with ½ cup sautéed mushrooms, chives, and 6 ounces of plain yogurt, or: 1-2-3 Breakfast of your choice (see page 4)

Lunch: Leftover Black Rice Chicken Congee, or:

Hearty Lentil Soup (recipe follows) with 2 slices of whole grain bread and 2 tablespoons almond butter per person

Dinner: Shrimp Pad Thai (recipe follows)

Snack: (Serves 1) 1 peach

HEARTY LENTIL SOUP (SERVES 4)

We love the simplicity of this soup—stir it all up and let it cook! It doesn't get much easier than this.

- 1 cup uncooked lentils
- 3 cups water
- 2 carrots, sliced
- 1 bell pepper, chopped
- 1 onion, chopped
- 2 red potatoes, chopped

- 2 tomatoes, chopped
- 1 teaspoon garam masala
- ½ teaspoon fresh ginger, grated
- 1 clove garlic, minced
- ¼ teaspoon red chili flakes
- Salt, to taste

Combine all ingredients in a large pot, stir well, and bring to a boil. Reduce heat to medium-low, cover, and cook for about 45 minutes, until all the vegetables are tender.

Week Four: Asian Heritage Diet

SHRIMP PAD THAI (SERVES 4)

This famous Thai noodle dish tastes even better than take-out!

- 8 ounces dried brown rice noodles
- 1 teaspoon cornstarch
- 1 teaspoon sesame oil
- 8 ounces raw shrimp, peeled and deveined
- ¼ cup1 tablespoon fish sauce
- ¼ cup fresh lemon juice (from 2 lemons)
- 3 tablespoons sugar
- 3 tablespoons canola oil, divided
- 3 large eggs, beaten

- 4 scallions, chopped
- 2 fresh red chili peppers, chopped
- 2 tablespoons garlic, minced
- 4 ounces firm tofu, cut into ½-inch cubes
- ½ cup bean sprouts
- ⅓ cup unsalted, roasted peanuts, chopped
- ¼ cup fresh basil leaves, cut into thin ribbons
- ¼ cup fresh cilantro leaves
- ½ teaspoon red pepper flakes

Soak the noodles in hot water until soft (about 20–30 minutes). Drain and cover. In a medium bowl, mix together the cornstarch and sesame oil. Toss the shrimp in the cornstarch mixture and let marinate for 15 minutes. In a small bowl, combine the fish sauce, lemon juice, and sugar. Heat a wok or a large frying pan over high heat. Add 2 tablespoons of oil and swirl until hot. Add the shrimp and cook, stirring constantly, for 30–40 seconds, until they turn pink. Remove to a sieve to drain. Add the egg to the pan, stirring vigorously until the egg has set. Remove to a plate. Pour in the last tablespoon of oil, add the scallions, red chilies, and garlic, and cook for 1 minute. Add the tofu, and stir gently for 1–2 minutes. Add the noodles and the fish sauce mixture, and stir well. Turn off the heat, and stir in the bean sprouts, peanuts, basil, cilantro, and red pepper flakes.

Day 25

Breakfast: Asian Breakfast Bowl (recipe follows), or: 1-2-3 Breakfast of your choice (see page 4)

Lunch: Leftover Shrimp Pad Thai (from Day 24), served with a green salad, or:

(Serves 1) 1 cup coleslaw mix served with ½ cup cooked quinoa (reserved from Asian Breakfast Bowl recipe), 2 scallions, ¼ cup sliced almonds, ½ red pepper, orange sections, Ginger Dressing (page 104)

Dinner: Chana Masala (Chickpeas) with Sweet Potatoes (recipe follows)

Snack: 1 mango

ASIAN BREAKFAST BOWL (SERVES 2)

Breakfast doesn't always have to be sweet. This breakfast bowl embraces bold, savory flavors that are delicious at any time of the day. Make extra quinoa and refrigerate to mix with coleslaw at lunch.

- 1 cup cooked brown rice or quinoa
- 2 eggs, whisked
- 1 teaspoon soy sauce
- 1 teaspoon sugar
- 1 scallion, chopped
- ½ teaspoon canola oil

- 1 cup spinach
- ¼ avocado, sliced
- 2 ounces smoked salmon
- ½ toasted nori seaweed sheet, torn or cut into strips

Warm your grains and set aside. Combine eggs, soy sauce, sugar, and scallion. Heat a small frying pan over medium heat, pour in the oil, and swirl to coat the pan. Pour in the egg mixture, and scramble the eggs. Top the warm grains with spinach, and place the hot eggs on top so that the greens wilt. Add avocado, salmon, and nori to the bowl and serve.

Week Four: Asian Heritage Diet

CHANA MASALA (CHICKPEAS) WITH SWEET POTATOES (SERVES 4)

Chana Masala is an Indian classic. In this version, we've added sweet potato and greens to make the dish even more interesting and satisfying. Make extra brown rice, if desired, for the breakfast congee recipe on Day 26.

- 1 tablespoon olive oil
- ½ large onion, chopped
- 1 teaspoon cumin
- ½ teaspoon cinnamon
- ½ teaspoon turmeric
- ½ teaspoon coriander
- ½ teaspoon ground cloves
- ¼ teaspoon red pepper flakes
- 1–2 cloves garlic, minced
- 1 tablespoon grated fresh ginger

- 1 (14.5-ounce) can chickpeas, drained and rinsed
- 1 (14.5-ounce) can diced tomatoes
- 1 large sweet potato
- ½ (13.5-ounce) can light coconut milk
- 1 cup brown rice
- 2 cups water
- 1 cup spinach, chopped
- Salt, to taste

Heat the oil in a large skillet, and cook the onion 4–5 minutes until soft and slightly golden. Add the dry spices. Add the garlic and ginger, then continue cooking gently for ten minutes to allow the flavors of the spices to combine with the onions. Add the chickpeas, tomatoes, sweet potatoes, and coconut milk. Bring to a boil, cover, and simmer on low for 45 minutes. In a separate pot, combine the brown rice and water, and bring to a boil. Lower heat, cover, and simmer for 40–50 minutes. Just before you're ready to serve, add the chopped greens to the bean mixture and cook for a few minutes until the greens are wilted. Add salt to taste, and serve with brown rice.

Day 26

Breakfast: (Serves 1) Black (or brown) rice breakfast congee: in a saucepan combine ½ cup cooked black rice (or use leftover brown rice from Day 25's dinner) and ¾ cup unsweetened almond milk. Simmer 15 minutes until thick and top with 1 tablespoon shredded coconut and 1 sliced banana, or: 1-2-3 Breakfast of your choice (see page 4)

Lunch: Leftover Chana Masala (Chickpeas) with Sweet Potatoes (from Day 25), or:

Vietnamese Chicken Salad (recipe follows) plus one whole wheat wrap per person

Dinner: Hearty Black Quinoa Slaw (recipe follows) served with ¼ cup of Asian Trail Mix (page 104) per person

Snack: (Serves 1) 1 plum

VIETNAMESE CHICKEN SALAD (SERVES 4)

This fresh, crunchy, chicken salad is great in a pita or wrap, on toast, or over salad.

- 1¼ pound chicken thigh fillets, cooked
- 1 cup thinly sliced celery
- 2 medium carrots, peeled and shredded
- 1 cup cabbage, finely shredded
- 3 scallions, chopped
- 3 tablespoons cilantro leaves
- 3 tablespoons mint, finely shredded
- ⅓ cup peanuts, chopped
- ⅓ cup Sweet and Sour Dressing (page 103)

Slice the chicken into long, thin strips. Combine the chicken, celery, carrot, cabbage, scallion, cilantro, mint, and peanuts in a large bowl. Pour the dressing over the chicken mixture and toss to combine.

Week Four: Asian Heritage Diet

HEARTY BLACK QUINOA SLAW WITH EDAMAME (SERVES 6)

Black quinoa is very pretty in this recipe with the brightly-colored vegetables, but any quinoa will work.

- 8 ounces black quinoa
- 2 cups water
- 2 cups red cabbage, shredded
- 1 cup shelled, steamed edamame
- 1 cup snap peas, chopped
- 1 cup carrots, shredded
- 1 cup scallions, chopped
- 1 mango, diced
- ½ cup fresh cilantro, chopped
- 1 cup Spicy Orange Ginger Dressing (page 103)
- 1 tablespoon sesame seeds, toasted

Rinse quinoa under cold water until water runs clear. Place quinoa in boiling water, then lower heat, and simmer for 12–15 minutes. In a large bowl combine cooked quinoa, red cabbage, edamame, snap peas, carrots, scallions, mango, and cilantro. Fold in the dressing and let it chill in the fridge. When ready to serve, garnish with toasted sesame seeds.

Recipe courtesy of InHarvest

Day 27

> **Breakfast:** Egg and Veggie Paratha (recipe follows), or: 1-2-3 Breakfast of your choice (see page 4)
>
> **Lunch:** Leftover Black Quinoa Slaw (from Day 26) in a whole wheat wrap with 2 ounces shredded chicken or grilled tofu, or:
>
> (Serves 1) Sushi rolls: Spread millet or brown rice in a thin layer on ⅓ of a nori sheet, add thinly sliced avocado, cucumber, smoked salmon, and carrot. Gently roll nori like a burrito, tucking in the sides as you go, rolling the filled side toward the un-filled side. Slice and chill.
>
> **Dinner:** Indonesian Red Rice Salad with Boiled Eggs and Macadamias (recipe follows)
>
> **Snack:** (Serves 1) 1 orange

EGG AND VEGGIE PARATHA (SERVES 2)

This recipe is a great way to use leftover vegetables. Finely chop broccoli, cabbage, or asparagus (or just about any other vegetable) as a substitute for the pepper and carrot.

- ½ cup whole wheat flour
- ¼ cup warm water, plus more if needed
- 3 eggs
- ½ onion, chopped
- 1 green chili, chopped
- ½ green pepper, chopped
- 1 small carrot, shredded
- Salt and pepper, to taste
- Pinch of turmeric
- 2 tablespoons cilantro, chopped
- Chutney, for serving

Mix flour and ¼ cup water in a bowl. Knead the dough, adding small amounts of water as necessary until the dough is pliable. Cover and set aside for 20 minutes. Separate dough into two balls and roll them out into ¼-inch-thick circles on floured surface. Heat dry frying pan over medium high heat. Place flattened dough on pan and cook until browned on both sides (dough will puff up and then deflate); remove from pan. Whisk together eggs, veggies, and spices. Oil the frying pan, lower heat to medium, and pour ½ egg mixture in. When egg is almost cooked, place one paratha on top of

egg in pan and press. Flip egg and paratha combination and cook for 2 minutes on the other side. Repeat for second serving. Serve with chutney.

INDONESIAN RED RICE SALAD WITH BOILED EGGS AND MACADAMIAS
(SERVES 6)

Indonesian cuisine is full of vibrant flavors and bright colors! The sweetness of the red rice is delicious in this dish, but brown rice would work well too.

- 1¾–2 cups water
- 1 cup red rice
- 2 tablespoons canola oil
- 4 large shallots, chopped
- 3 cloves garlic, chopped
- 1 large red chili, seeded and chopped
- 1-inch piece fresh ginger, chopped
- 1 teaspoon ground coriander
- 1 large carrot, thinly sliced
- 8 ounces green beans, trimmed and chopped
- ½ cup coconut milk
- 2 tablespoons soy sauce
- 4 large eggs, boiled, peeled and slice lengthwise
- 1 large lime, quartered
- ½ cup fresh basil, cut in thin strips
- ¼ cup chopped macadamia nuts, toasted

In a saucepan, bring water to a boil. Rinse the rice and drain. Add rice to boiling water and reduce heat to low; cook according to package directions (30–45 minutes). When cooking has finished, let cool to room temperature. In a large frying pan, heat the oil over high heat. Add the shallots, garlic, chili, ginger, coriander, carrot, and green beans. Stir-fry until the vegetables are crisp-tender. Add the coconut milk and soy sauce to the pan, and bring to a boil. Push the vegetables over to one side of the pan to make room for the eggs. Place the boiled eggs in the pan, cut sides down. Simmer for 2 minutes. In a large bowl, mix the contents of the pan with the rice. Add the basil and macadamias, then toss and serve.

Recipe courtesy of Robin Asbell, author of *300 Best Blender Recipes*, *Great Bowls of Food*, *The Whole Grain Promise*, and more. **robinasbell.com**

Day 28

Breakfast: Orange Cardamom Millet Porridge (recipe follows) or: 1-2-3 Breakfast of your choice (see page 4)

Lunch: Leftover Indonesian Red Rice Salad with Boiled Eggs and Macadamias (from Day 27), served with ½ cup steamed edamame, or:

(Serves 1) Lettuce wraps: two large leaves of romaine or bibb lettuce each filled with ⅓ cup brown rice, 2 ounces baked fish (of your choosing), and 3 florets of steamed broccoli (or other leftover vegetable), and drizzled with Ginger Dressing (page 104). Serve with a small green salad.

Dinner: Stir-Fried Thai Sorghum Bowl (recipe follows)

Snack: ½ cup whole grain crackers served with 2 tablespoons peanut butter

ORANGE CARDAMOM MILLET PORRIDGE (SERVES 4)

Millet makes wonderfully creamy porridge. With orange juice and dates to sweeten it, and cardamom to make it fragrant, this porridge tastes truly decadent.

- 2 cups water
- ⅔ cup uncooked millet
- 1½ cups orange juice
- 4 dates, pitted and chopped
- ¼ teaspoon ground cinnamon
- ¼ teaspoon ground cardamom
- Pinch of salt
- Orange slices, fresh or canned

In a medium pot, combine water, millet, orange juice, dates, cinnamon, cardamom, and salt, and bring to a boil. Reduce heat to low, cover and simmer, stirring occasionally until millet is tender and porridge has thickened, about 30 minutes. Serve and top with orange slices.

STIR-FRIED THAI SORGHUM BOWL (SERVES 4)

Sorghum is an ancient grain that's making a huge comeback. It's a great addition to salads, soups, and even omelets.

- 4 teaspoons peanut oil, divided
- 2 cups asparagus spears, chopped
- 2 carrots, peeled and sliced
- 1 tablespoon ginger, grated
- 2 cloves garlic, minced
- 1 tablespoon water
- 1 red bell pepper, cored, seeded, and sliced
- 1½ cups snow peas, sliced
- 1 tablespoon low-sodium soy sauce
- 1 (15-ounce) package extra-firm tofu, pressed for 30 minutes and cut into 1-inch cubes
- 1¾ cups Thai Peanut Sauce (page 104)
- 2 cups cooked sorghum, warmed

Heat 2 teaspoons of peanut oil in a large frying pan or wok over medium-high heat. Add the asparagus, carrots, ginger, and garlic, and stir fry for 1 minute. Add the water to the skillet and cover; let the vegetables steam for about 2 minutes until they become bright and tender. Add the red pepper, snow peas, and soy sauce to the pan. Cook, stirring constantly, for 3–4 minutes or more. Remove the vegetables and wipe the pan clean with a paper towel. Return the skillet to medium-high heat. Add the remaining peanut oil and swirl to coat, then add the tofu. Cook until lightly browned and crisp on all sides, turning occasionally, for about 5 minutes. Pour Thai Peanut Sauce over the tofu. Cook for 4–5 minutes until the sauce has thickened and the tofu is coated. Return the vegetables to the pan, and toss once more to coat. Divide the cooked sorghum between 4 bowls and top with the vegetables and tofu.

Recipe courtesy of Sharon Palmer, RD, The Plant-Powered Dietitian™

Stir-Fried Thai Sorghum Bowl

(recipe pg.97)

Coconut Fish Curry with Mango

(recipe pg.85)

Resources

Sauces, Dressings, and Snacks

DILL YOGURT SAUCE
(Makes about 1 cup) **4 SERVINGS**

- 1 cup plain Greek yogurt
- Juice of 1 lemon
- 2 tablespoons fresh dill
- Capers (optional garnish)

Mix all of the ingredients in a small bowl until well-combined. It makes an excellent topping for fish, or as a dip for vegetables.

BALSAMIC VINAIGRETTE
(Makes ¾ cup) **6 SERVINGS**

- ¼ cup balsamic vinegar
- ½ cup olive oil
- ¼ teaspoon salt

Combine all of the ingredients in a jar with a tight-fitting lid, and shake until well blended.

LEMON HERB VINAIGRETTE
(Makes 1 cup) **8 SERVINGS**

- ¼ cup wine vinegar
- Juice of 1 lemon
- ½ cup olive oil
- ¼ teaspoon salt
- 1 tablespoon fresh rosemary

Mix all of the ingredients in a jar with a tight-fitting lid, and shake until well blended.

HERB VINAIGRETTE
(Makes ¾ cup) **6 SERVINGS**

- ¼ cup vinegar (cider or wine)
- ½ cup olive oil
- Salt and pepper, to taste
- 1 tablespoon fresh chopped herbs, such as basil, oregano, rosemary, parsley, or tarragon

Mix all of the ingredients in a jar with a tight-fitting lid, and shake until well blended.

CABBAGE AND CARROT SLAW
(Makes 2 cups) **2 SERVINGS**

- 1 cup carrots, shredded
- 1 cup cabbage, shredded
- 1 tablespoon sesame seeds

For the dressing:

- ¼ cup vinegar (cider or wine)
- 2 tablespoons olive oil
- 1 clove garlic, minced
- 1 teaspoon Dijon mustard
- 1 teaspoon honey
- Salt and pepper, to taste

Mix the carrot, cabbage and sesame seeds in a large bowl. In a small bowl, combine vinegar, oil, garlic, mustard, honey, salt and pepper. Pour dressing over the carrot and cabbage mixture, and mix thoroughly.

Sauces, Dressings, and Snacks

DIJON VINAIGRETTE
(Makes ⅓ cup) **4 SERVINGS**

- 2 tablespoons apple cider vinegar
- Juice of 1 lime
- 1 teaspoon Dijon mustard
- 1 teaspoon honey
- ¼ cup olive oil
- Half a small shallot, finely diced (optional)
- ½ teaspoon ground cumin
- ½ teaspoon cayenne pepper
- Salt and pepper, to taste

Whisk together the vinegar, lime juice, mustard, and honey in a small bowl. Drizzle in the olive oil gradually, whisking to combine, then add the shallot, cumin, cayenne, salt and pepper, and whisk until combined.

MANGO PAPAYA SALAD
4 SERVINGS

- 3 mangoes, peeled, pitted, and chopped
- 1 papaya, peeled, deseeded and chopped
- 4 tablespoons coconut milk
- 1 teaspoon honey or agave syrup

Mix the all the ingredients together gently in a large bowl. Serve chilled or at room temperature.

CILANTRO LIME CREMA
(Makes 1¼ cups) **6 SERVINGS**

- 1 cup plain yogurt or silken tofu
- Juice of 3 limes
- 2 tablespoons fresh cilantro

Mix all of the ingredients in a small bowl until well combined.

LIME VINAIGRETTE
(Makes 1 cup) **8 SERVINGS**

- ¼ cup wine vinegar
- Juice of 2 limes
- ½ cup extra-virgin olive oil
- ¼ teaspoon salt

Combine all of the ingredients in a jar with a tight-fitting lid, and shake until well blended.

GUACAMOLE
(Makes 1 cup) **4 SERVINGS**

- 1 ripe avocado
- 1 lime, quartered
- Sea salt, to taste

Open the avocado and scoop out the flesh. Mash with a fork or a spoon. Squeeze the lime juice, and add to the avocado. Add salt to taste, mix well.

Sauces, Dressings, and Snacks

SOFRITO (Makes about 2 cups)
4 SERVINGS

Sofrito is a rich, vegetable-based purée that adds deep flavor to many soups, stews and sauces. "Red sofritos"—made with tomatoes and/or roasted red peppers—originated in Spain and shows up in many Hispanic-Caribbean dishes, while "green sofritos" are also a common building block in Latin-American cuisine. In this book, we use sofrito as a topping for cornmeal polenta and in Arroz Con Pollo.

- 2 tablespoons extra-virgin olive oil
- 2 cloves garlic, minced
- 1 yellow onion, chopped
- 8 medium plum tomatoes (or 1 (28-ounce) can whole tomatoes)
- 2 sprigs fresh parsley, chopped
- 4 sprigs fresh thyme, leaves removed (or ⅛ teaspoon dried thyme)
- ½ teaspoon salt
- ¼ teaspoon black pepper

Heat the oil in a large skillet over medium heat until it ripples. Add the garlic and onion and sauté, stirring, for 2 minutes. Add the tomatoes, herbs, salt, and pepper, breaking apart the tomatoes with a spoon as they cook. Reduce the heat and simmer for 20 to 30 minutes. Taste and adjust seasoning.

SWEET AND SOUR DRESSING
(Makes about ⅓ cup) **2 SERVINGS**

- 1 tablespoon honey
- 2 tablespoons water
- 1 teaspoon garlic, crushed
- 2 tablespoons rice vinegar
- 1 red chili, seeded and finely chopped

Place all the ingredients in a small bowl and whisk until the honey is dissolved.

SPICY ORANGE GINGER DRESSING
(Makes about 1 cup) **8 SERVINGS**

- ½ cup orange juice
- ¼ cup rice wine vinegar
- 2 tablespoons minced fresh ginger
- 1 teaspoon Sriracha sauce
- ¼ cup sesame oil

In a small bowl, combine the orange juice, rice wine vinegar, ginger and Sriracha sauce. Slowly whisk in sesame oil until well combined.

Sauces, Dressings, and Snacks

ASIAN TRAIL MIX
8 SERVINGS

- ½ cups peanut
- ¼ cup cashews
- ¼ cup macadamia nuts
- ¼ cup blanched almonds
- 1 teaspoon ground black pepper
- 1 teaspoon cinnamon
- 1 teaspoon salt
- ¼ cup raisins
- ¼ cup golden raisins (can add more raisins)
- ¼ cup candied ginger

Preheat the oven to 300°F. In a large bowl, toss all of the nuts with spices, salt, and sugar. Spread them evenly on a baking sheet and bake for about 15 to 20 minutes, checking them every 5 minutes and shaking the sheet occasionally to redistribute them so they will brown evenly. Remove them from the oven when they are lightly browned. When they are fully cooled, combine the seasoned nuts with the dried fruit and candied ginger. Store the trail mix in an airtight container.

GINGER DRESSING
(Makes 1¼ cups) **10 SERVINGS**

- ½ cup olive oil
- ¼ cup balsamic vinegar
- 2 tablespoons low-sodium soy sauce
- 1 teaspoon toasted sesame oil
- 2 cloves garlic, roughly chopped
- 2 tablespoons honey
- 2 tablespoons fresh ginger, minced

Mix all of the ingredients in a small bowl until well combined.

THAI PEANUT SAUCE
(Makes 1¾ cups) **4 SERVINGS**

- 1 cup light coconut milk
- 1 tablespoon Thai red curry paste
- ⅓ cup creamy peanut butter
- 1 tablespoon low-sodium soy sauce
- 2 ½ tablespoons maple syrup
- 1 garlic clove, minced
- 2 teaspoons fresh ginger, minced
- 1 teaspoon cornstarch

Mix all of the ingredients in a small bowl until well combined.

Recipe Index and Nutritional Information

Page	Recipe	Calories	Fat (g)	Sat Fat (g)	Sodium (g)	Carbs (g)	Fiber (g)	Sugar (g)	Protein (g)
58	African Peanut Soup	320	14	2.5	460	36	8	8	12
72	Amaranth with Peppers and Cabbage	160	8	1	170	19	4	4	4
77	Arroz con Pollo (Rice with Chicken)	410	13	2	560	41	3	3	30
90	Asian Breakfast Bowl	340	13	2	250	29	4	3	27
104	Asian Trail Mix	180	12	2	300	17	2	11	4
40	Avocado Tuna Salad in a Pita Pocket	250	10	1.5	520	24	4	3	19
101	Balsamic Vinaigrette	170	18	0.5	100	2	0	2	0
78	Banana Amaranth Porridge	360	8	4	80	58	8	17	13
73	Barley, Pineapple, and Jicama Salad with Avocado	390	19	3	125	51	16	8	7
76	Beans and Greens	180	8	1	440	23	11	1	8
87	Black Rice Chicken Congee	630	35	6	540	53	9	5	28
50	Black-Eyed Pea Salad Wrap	250	4	1	170	44	5	6	11
101	Cabbage and Carrot Slaw	200	16	2	400	11	3	7	2
61	Caribbean Coconut Red Beans	210	4.5	3	400	33	8	2	11
91	Chana Masala (Chickpeas) with Sweet Potatoes	470	13	4.5	550	78	12	11	13
102	Cilantro Lime Crema	30	0.5	0	30	5	0	3	2
85	Coconut Fish Curry with Mango and Sugar Snap Peas	290	16	5	310	25	3	17	13
52	Curried Couscous with Peppers	390	7	0.5	290	68	6	9	15
102	Dijon Vinaigrette	130	14	2	170	3	0	2	0
101	Dill Yogurt Sauce	35	0	0	20	3	0	2	6

Recipe Index and Nutritional Information

Page	Recipe	Calories	Fat (g)	Sat Fat (g)	Sodium (g)	Carbs (g)	Fiber (g)	Sugar (g)	Protein (g)
94	Egg and Veggie Paratha	230	7	2	460	29	6	3	13
79	Enchilada Casserole	320	11	5	630	45	6	6	23
66	Fiesta Quinoa Salad	400	10	1.5	770	66	13	6	15
69	Fish Tacos with Mango Salsa	670	33	4.5	860	63	11	26	35
31	Freekeh Pilaf	280	14	1.5	100	34	6	3	8
104	Ginger Dressing	120	11	1.5	115	6	0	4	0
102	Guacamole	90	7	1	150	6	4	1	1
93	Hearty Black Quinoa Slaw with Edamame	370	16	2	60	50	8	16	10
88	Hearty Lentil Soup	270	1	0	200	54	9	8	15
101	Herb Vinaigrette	160	18	2.5	100	0	0	0	0
32	Herb-Baked Fish	150	6	2	120	0	0	0	23
49	Herb-Crusted Tilapia and Garlicky Dill Greens	300	13	2	330	19	3	4	30
95	Indonesian Red Rice Salad with Boiled Eggs and Macadamias	500	25	9	550	56	5	9	16
55	Jollof Rice	390	9	1.5	270	70	7	8	8
84	Kimchi Soba Noodles	400	14	1.5	170	61	1	4	10
101	Lemon Herb Vinaigrette	120	14	2	75	0	0	0	0
102	Lime Vinaigrette	120	14	2	75	1	0	0	0
102	Mango Papaya Salad	200	4	3	10	44	5	38	3
60	Maple Walnut Teff Porridge	530	25	12	320	69	11	6	13
39	Mediterranean Eggplant and Barley Salad	330	9	1	410	53	17	7	12

Information provided by the Whole Grains Council

wholegrainscouncil.org

Recipe Index and Nutritional Information

Page	Recipe	Calories	Fat (g)	Sat Fat (g)	Sodium (g)	Carbs (g)	Fiber (g)	Sugar (g)	Protein (g)
35	Mediterranean Pita Pizza	320	9	1.5	350	51	1	4	14
48	Millet with Zucchini and Chickpeas	430	12	1.5	430	68	12	9	14
57	Moroccan Tagine with Prunes	460	18	3	610	50	10	13	26
70	Mosh (Guatemalan Oatmeal)	210	4.5	2	135	32	2	19	13
67	Oldways Wild Veggie Tostadas	306	7	1	322	42	9	3	9
68	Oldways' Easy Huevos Rancheros	460	17	3.5	590	57	20	8	22
96	Orange Cardamom Millet Porridge	240	1.5	0	150	53	5	24	5
38	Pasta e Fagioli	190	4	1	540	29	9	4	9
54	Quinoa Porridge with Figs and Honey	420	20	2	50	55	9	24	11
51	Quinoa with Ginger and Carrots	280	7	1	180	45	6	3	10
75	Sauteed Quinoa with Swiss Chard	210	6	1	710	32	4	2	7
30	Shish Kebabs	290	14	2	210	13	2	9	29
89	Shrimp Pad Thai	560	24	4	750	65	2	13	25
36	Slow Cooker Greek Gigante Beans	340	1	0	410	65	20	13	20
103	Sofrito	110	7	1	520	10	4	5	2
74	South American Vegetable and Rice Soup	320	3	0.5	390	66	10	10	10
59	Southern-Style Chicken and Wild Rice Pilaf	300	12	2	280	38	3	14	11
42	Spaghetti with Mussels and Tomato Sauce	470	14	4.5	530	66	2	9	25

Information provided by the Whole Grains Council

wholegrainscouncil.org

Recipe Index and Nutritional Information

Page	Recipe	Calories	Fat (g)	Sat Fat (g)	Sodium (g)	Carbs (g)	Fiber (g)	Sugar (g)	Protein (g)
103	Spicy Orange Ginger Dressing	70	7	1	20	3	0	1	0
56	Spinach Cucumber Dill Salad	230	6	1	250	33	5	4	6
41	Steel Cut Oat Risotto with Mushrooms	630	19	5	610	98	10	18	25
97	Stir-Fried Thai Sorghum Bowl	210	4	0.5	390	39	9	5	8
71	Stuffed Poblanos	45	0	0	0	11	0	10	1
103	Sweet and Sour Dressing	60	0	0	310	13	4	1	3
33	Tabbouleh	160	5	0.5	290	22	14	3	11
53	Tangy Collard Greens	110	10	2.5	440	15	0	10	1
104	Thai Peanut Sauce	60	0	0	690	8	0	4	6
86	Tom Yang Goong	220	14	3.5	120	11	2	4	12
34	Veggie Omelet with Farro	350	18	4.5	170	7	3	4	39
92	Vietnamese Chicken Salad	320	9	1.5	330	47	7	3	19
37	Whole Grain Pasta with Sardines and Swiss Chard	300	13	2	330	19	3	4	30

Information provided by the Whole Grains Council   wholegrainscouncil.org

Index

Index

Index

Index

Index

Grains Cooking Chart

Whole grains are a must in any food lover's pantry, as few other foods can so beautifully transform a medley of produce into a hearty, satiating meal. The perfect partner to any ingredient, whole grains also lend a rich variety of flavors, textures, and aromas to your dishes.

To 1 cup of...	Add this much water or broth:	Bring to a boil, then simmer for:	Yields:
Amaranth	2 cups	20 to 25 minutes	3 ½ cups
Barley, hulled	3 cups	45 to 60 minutes	3 ½ cups
Buckwheat	2 cups	20 minutes	4 cups
Bulgur	2 cups	10 to 12 minutes	3 cups
Cornmeal (polenta)	4 cups	25 to 30 minutes	2½ cups
Couscous, whole wheat	2 cups	10 minutes (heat off)	3 cups
Kamut® wheat	4 cups	Soak overnight, then cook 45 to 60 minutes	3 cups
Millet, hulled	2½ cups	25 to 35 minutes	4 cups
Oats, steel cut	4 cups	20 minutes	4 cups
Pasta, whole wheat	6 cups	8 to 12 minutes (varies by size)	Varies
Quinoa	2 cups	12 to 15 minutes	3+ cups
Rice, brown	2½ cups	25 to 45 minutes (varies by variety)	3–4 cups
Rye berries	4 cups	Soak overnight, then cook 45 to 60 minutes	3 cups
Sorghum	4 cups	25 to 40 minutes	3 cups
Spelt berries	4 cups	Soak overnight, then cook 45 to 60 minutes	3 cups
Teff	3 to 4 cups	15 to 20 minutes	3 cups
Wheat berries	4 cups	Soak overnight, then cook 45 to 60 minutes	3 cups
Wild rice	3 cups	45 to 55 minutes	3½ cups

Information provided by the Whole Grains Council   wholegrainscouncil.org